BRESSBEE THE ICE KING

BRESSBEE THE ICE KING

Rebecca Walters

Published by Rebecca Walters
YouCaxton Publications
23 High Street, Bishop's Castle, Shropshire, SY9 5BE
www.YouCaxton.co.uk

ISBN 978-0-9573316-0-0

Printed in Great Britain

Author's Note

In her warm and cosy farmhouse kitchen, in the sandstone cottage nestled into Tedsmore Hill, my buddy Clare Jones stood proudly under a framed photo hanging on her wall. She stood proudly because she was telling me the history behind the picture. The story of the chestnut horse she fell in love with, trained and then took to St. Moritz to win. As she tells me the tale I can see the love, the life and the memories dancing behind her smiling eyes. After sitting quietly, sipping my cup of tea, soaking up the highs and lows of the tale my response was simply;

"That's a bloody book isn't it?"

So I wrote the book, and here it is. I truly hope I have done Bressbee justice and that as the reader, you enjoy it. Bressbee's story is a British sporting achievement, one that should be recognised and admired for the incredible accomplishment it is. I would like to thank Clare and James for allowing me to write the book. Jonesy, what can I say? Except put the kettle on, I'll have two sugars today. James, I hope you don't cringe too much!

Thanks to Jennifer Parratt & Irene Macro for giving me the structure and editing the book.

Thanks also to Les Hurley & Country Style Photography.

Special thanks to my unconditional buddy Lou, you might not think it but you're an inspiration.

Diane, Laura & Lynn you've all been generous in time and effort, without your help the book wouldn't be here.

Thank you to my husband, you can have the laptop back now and perhaps your wife!

Joseph, my little "Bloody Gorgeous" I will help you write your story now, and Jack, my "Chicken Pie", yes, you can have some free copies to sell to your mates on the bus to make a few quid!

I cannot let it go to print without mentioning my legendary Grandfather, Leonard Norton.

"Nort" you are missed every day, and if you were here you'd be saying "Watch that racing lark, don't start gambling, it's a mugs game!"

I'm being a good girl, filling my home with love and laughter, just like you told me to.

"Who loves you baby?"

Contents

Prologue

Right here, right now.
Radiating against the blanket beneath.
Sculpted and honed to perfection.

Right here, right now.
Noise muted except the inhale and exhale.
Billowing breath, warm against the chill.

Right here, right now.
Absorbed in anticipation.
Cutting into the crisp, shifting inside the space.

Right here, right now.
Waiting to win.

Chapter One

13th June 2002

"Got him! Talk later."

James Unett read the curt message which had just arrived on his phone. The briefest of smiles teased the corners of his lips before normal service was resumed with a scowl. The phone irritated him, disturbing the precious little rest he had in the afternoon before evening stable duties. Yet this was the type of interruption he enjoyed. He laid his head back, relaxing into the large, brown leather sofa, distressed through years of use. This could be good for business. His business was a game of numbers, and James Unett was almost winning.

James cast his eyes over his surroundings, taking in the crumbling mountain of back copies of the Racing Post which lay on the floor, and the bills that lay unopened on the coffee table in front of him, vying for position with cigarette ends in the already overflowing ashtray. He lit a cigarette carefully, inhaling deeply with his first breath and exhaling slowly, satiated. He looked at the threadbare rug on the floor of the lounge, the setting for the wooden cabinet in the corner of the room, its drawers partially open, inviting James to organise his affairs. He ignored their plea and instead looked out of the large window to his left. Being a resident trainer at Dunstall Park, Wolverhampton, was not the salubrious position one would think. James and his partner Clare had one of the two barns, two sand paddocks and a mid-terrace house next to the course. From there James trained horses for both flat and national hunt races. He knew the benefits of being a trainer 'on track' and his business profited from them. For the owners, having a horse in training with the resident trainer of a track meant fewer travel costs to and from race meets and since the horse is running 'at home' they are comfortable with the environment within which they are expected to perform at their optimum ability.

From his viewpoint on the sofa he could see the sand school and three youngsters making their way across the yard on exercise. To the left of the school the barn to the stables was open. James frowned at the sight of hay and shavings littering the floor. A stable hand was brushing manically, fighting a losing battle to keep the agricultural intruders from occupying the walkways. He'd have to talk to them about their technique, he thought. Swinging his legs off the sofa, James sat up, resting his elbows on his knees and holding his head in his hands. The cigarette smoke billowed across the room like layers of cotton wool. James sat like that for some time, quietly processing the text and what it would mean to him and the yard.

Jolted from his thoughts, James heard the back door open. The fresh air sucked the smoke from the room like a vacuum. Clare kicked off her riding boots and pulled the door shut behind her. Flicking the kettle on as she passed it and grabbing the morning's post she made her way to the lounge. As she moved, she carved a path through the cigarette smoke, parting it like Moses through the Red Sea. Complaining about the smoke in the house, she flopped on the sofa next to James. Having mucked out twelve horses and ridden five, that morning, she was shattered.

"No use sitting down there Jonesy," muttered James through the smoke. "Alistair claimed that horse Bressbee out of a Seller at Brighton. He just text me, so you'd better get a box ready!"

Clare smiled drowsily from behind closed eyes. "It's already done! What's this one like then? Anything I need to know?" Her voice was then hushed by the sound of the kettle whistling. She slid off the sofa to make the tea, stepping through the steam which was creeping round the door frame.

"Four year old, Irish bred gelding," James responded, preoccupied. He was searching through Ceefax for the racing results of the day, trying to find out how well Bressbee had run. Had he been placed or had he finished out at the back of the television screen? Agonisingly

slowly, the results filtered into view. The intermittent, flashing cursor rushes for no man. James finally found what he was looking for:

The Alexander Catering Events Selling Stakes for three-five year olds.

Distance: 1m 1f 209 yards

Going: Good to soft

Jockey: Fergus Sweeney

Bressbee had led for the first furlong, remained prominent, rode hard over 1 furlong and finished fifth. James grunted and nodded his head. "That'll do," he thought.

"Does that mean that Alistair and that awful Miranda will be hovering about again?" Clare asked, popping her head around the door frame. James just gave her a knowing nod. She knew full well the answer to the question was yes, but she was making her views on the couple clear from the outset. She didn't like them and they didn't like her! It would mean James jumping through hoops once again, in order to please yet another over-expectant and self-indulgent owner. Fabulous!

James first encountered Alistair thanks to an existing happy customer, who had two horses placed at James' training yard in Wolverhampton. The happy customer was a business colleague of Alistair's. Alistair, true to form, didn't want to be outdone by his colleague who described James as the 'trainer that gets results.' He had immediately made it his mission to buy another racehorse and place it at James' yard. He made a visit, with his wife, to Dunstall Park, where Clare and James entertained them for an afternoon, showing them the yard and introducing the horses. As James and Alistair talked through figures in the office, Clare walked Miranda through the barn explaining the breeding and background behind each horse in training. As Clare passed each box, its resident would poke an enquiring head over the door and very often nuzzle into Clare. A cheeky yearling that was in for breaking tried to nestle into Miranda's shoulder, and as the young horse did so it inhaled Miranda's strong perfume, causing it to promptly sneeze all over her! Miranda shrieked like a wild gibbon and made for the ladies toilet as though she was running a 5 furlong sprint! That spelled the end of the yard walk for Clare and Miranda, and James decided to defuse the situation by giving the couple tickets to the race meet for that evening. This would give Alistair and Miranda an opportunity to familiarise themselves with the course and more importantly for Miranda to acquaint herself with the Owners and Trainers lounge.

Despite being the first track to be floodlit in Britain, plans to fully modernise Dunstall Park were in the final stages of planning, awaiting approval. The promise of a modern and vibrant grandstand at the UK's busiest track was a very enticing prospect for the Cavendish couple. Miranda loved it that a flat horse could run all year with no break in the season. She wasn't a fan of jump racing or standing in a wet and muddy field. Squinting through her carefully made up eyes, while attempting to see an animal whizzing around a white rail in the distance, wasn't her idea of fun. The awful British weather invariably ruined her hair, which although poker straight, was secretly frizzy and unmanageable. Two races into the last point to point meet they had attended, the drizzle had well and truly set in and before long her perfect Cleopatra look had made way for Planet of the Apes!

After having made clear the extremely professional requirements that they demanded of their new horse, the Cavendish's returned home, leaving James dumbstruck by their ignorance and dumb founded by the task that they had set him. Finding a horse to meet their exacting requirements was not going to be easy. Reaching for the programme book, James thumbed through for Selling and Claiming races (races that are run by horses that are subsequently for sale). He highlighted any potential horses that would be pleasing to Mrs Cavendish.

One stood out from the rest, Bressbee. A 16.1hh flat racer, entered in a Selling race in Brighton on the 13th June. Bred in Ireland he carried bloodlines known for galloping on the dirt tracks of the USA. Born on the 23rd January 1998 he was a four year old gelding sired by Twining an 8 1/2 furlong winner and came out of Bressay an 8 furlong winner. However despite all the breeding, the selection and the promise, Bressbee wasn't cutting the mustard. On paper he should be well suited to the 'all-weather track' at Dunstall Park. The surface of which is 'Polytrack', a synthetic material that provides a more or less consistent feel for the horses running on it. Similar to the dirt tracks his Sire and Dam had traversed throughout their careers. That is what caught James' eye.

He had shown promise as a young horse, winning as a three year old and being regularly placed second or third across his races. A

decent performer at that time, Bressbee was a horse that had regularly been in the frame, however recently seemed to have become a bit stale. James believed that with Clare's help they could turn him around. Although the horse may have thus far lacked that serious 'X factor', and his motivation for the job was leaving a lot to be desired, the Cavendish's wouldn't care. He was a good enough horse to tick their boxes. And he was the right colour according to Miranda's demanding list. After all chestnuts were striking. James decided to send Alistair and Miranda to the track to watch him race and bid for him themselves. James knew it would be a circus. Sellers and Claimers usually were, but he had no doubt that this pair of monkeys would fit right in.

James and Clare sat on the sofa with newly brewed cups of tea in hand. Together they calculated when Bressbee would arrive at the yard.

"Brighton to Wolverhampton, six hours, including stops and a careful driver," James estimated.

"Sounds reasonable," said Clare. "He raced at 1pm, factor in jockey weigh-in, bidding and claims, they should leave by 3pm. We can have him tucked up in bed by nine tonight."

James nodded his agreement and drained his mug.

****

In Brighton, Alistair drained his glass of Cristal, and watched his wife stumble off to the stabling area to welcome their new horse. He knew he had had far too much to drink, and a slight look of concern spread across his face as he thought his wife was in a more inebriated state than himself.

His concerned look turned to one of alarm as he heard his wife's high pitched screams.

"He is my horsh! And I want to give him a kissh. Take your handsh off me you idiot!"

Alistair halted his dash to be by her side. Sometimes, he thought, she was just a little uncouth!

He watched as his drunken wife was removed from the stabling area by the stewards. He wasn't surprised. Security was always overzealous in these places. He overheard the stewards mutter about racing rules and proof of ownership, when he decided to step in and save her from the embarrassment she was causing both to herself and him by association.

"Sorry gentlemen, she's had a few too many celebratory glasses. We bought a horse you know!" Alistair started but was met with a stony stare from the steward. Determined not to be put off, Alistair continued. "He'll be a great winner for us, it's all so exciting! He has a place at Dunstall Park, on the track. Next time you see us, you'll be buying us a drink."

Again the steward remained unmoved. "I think you've missed your lift," he said abruptly, nodding his head in the direction of the trainer he had been advised to talk to about transporting Bressbee back to the Midlands.

"Bugger," exclaimed Alistair as the trainer drove off in the lorry and headed off to the Midlands without Bressbee.

Fraught that he had purchased a horse that he now had no way of transporting, Alistair approached every man in the lounge wearing a trainers tag, desperate to find anyone willing to drive his horse to James' yard. After much wailing, whinging and wringing of hands, it was arranged that Bressbee would have to do the journey in two stages. The first leg would take him to a yard in Long Mountain, South Wales, with a trainer called Rob Hughes. Then the following day, that same lorry was leaving to travel north up the country and they would deliver Bressbee to Dunstall Park en route. Alistair was parched with relief that he had managed to organise the travel arrangements. He ordered another glass of Cristal and set about removing his, by then severely intoxicated wife, from the Owners and Trainers lounge. She sat slumped silent in the corner of the room, her black glossy mane tousled and unkempt. He thought she looked rather attractive. In one long swallow, he drained his glass and called his driver to take them home, forgetting in his lustful haze to inform James of the arrangements. Without even checking Bressbee had been loaded onto the correct lorry, he bundled Miranda into the back of her new blue BMW M3, and their driver tore away from the course homeward bound.

Bressbee stood in his box in Brighton, quietly listening to the yard around him. His chiselled, elegant head hung over the door observing the yard. His eyes and nostrils tinged with darker pigment, his muzzle soft and velvety. Central to his forehead was a crisp white star, the only white on his entire, conker coloured body. Standing tall in his box, he had presence and energy. Not the usual fine boned flat horse, he looked more dual purpose with width and bone. He wouldn't have looked out

of place in a national hunt yard. His huge shoulders and rump made anyone up close feel his raw power. His short neatly trimmed mane highlighted his toned neck, accentuating his athleticism.

Most of the horses who had raced that day had been led away, back to the lorry park for loading. There was just him and another horse on the end of the row waiting to go home. She was a small filly, two years old and very flashy. Her iron grey coat made her stand out from the crowd, she had a big white blaze running the length of her elegant head and all four of her feet were white. She was getting cold. After running so hard she was tired and her old stable lad had gone without putting her rug on. She shifted to the back of her stable to avoid the draught from the door.

Bressbee himself was tired and bored. He was bored of racing, bored of running, just bored! He slumped with his head dropped to his knees and sighed loudly. He could never relax at the races, there were too many people, too much noise and too many unfamiliar smells. He picked up his head once more, rested it on top of the stable door and with ears pricked stared blinking at the gate. Soon someone would come.

That someone was a rather rotund man, ruddy faced and burly. Glyn had driven for Rob Hughes for years. He had been asked to take two horses back to Long Mountain but decided to have another pint before he left and miss the heavy traffic. Bressbee's box was his next stop.

"Where's that damn head collar laddy?" he cursed, searching around the stable block. He bumped into the wall and hit his head on the top door, before finding it hanging behind the door ready for transport. Bressbee was confused. This wasn't his normal type of handling and he didn't quite know what to make of this man trying to look after him. He decided to comply, placing his nose in the head collar ready to leave.

"Not a bad sort, are ya? I'm Glyn, nice to make your acquaintance. Now, get a move on and let's get to Wales." Glyn chatted to Bressbee as if he was an old friend and Bressbee liked it. His door swung open, and he led Glyn to the box, ready to go home. Alerted by the movement on the yard, the little grey filly rushed to the door and whinnied. She was not happy at being left on the yard and as Bressbee was led away he could hear her squealing in her box, kicking the walls with her racing plates protesting about her entrapment.

Glyn could hear the filly getting stressed in her box. Aware of the money involved in the racehorse game, he hurried Bressbee onto the lorry so as to get back to her as quickly and as safely as possible. In doing so, he tied Bressbee's head to the ring inside the lorry too tightly so he could hardly move. His head collar was digging into his nose and cheek, the pain making him wince. His head was unnaturally high, held there by the rope. Bressbee whinnied in complaint, hoping Glyn would notice. But Glyn was nowhere to be seen. He had rushed back across the yard to settle the filly, who had trashed her box and was proving very difficult to catch, even in such a confined space. After a struggle, Glyn managed to get a chifney bit on her and talked to her quietly as he tried to lead her across the yard.

"There you go doll, no need to panic. Damn thoroughbreds! All the same, calm down now. Here's the ginger boy to keep you company."

But the filly was so strung out by that point that she went up in the air and danced for two steps. Feeling the chifney take effect, she dropped back down onto all four feet, then stood on her two front feet, hind legs thrashing about behind her. She plunged and dived across the yard, until she found herself at the bottom of the ramp and there she intended to stay. Not in the lorry and not back in the stables. She planted all four feet on terra firma and would not move.

Bressbee could not see what happened next, all he knew was that after lots of shouting and shoving the filly finally stood next to him, quivering and trembling. Her grey coat was black with sweat. He could hear Glyn walking round the lorry and he realised that in the panic to get the filly on the lorry, Glyn had forgotten to re-check his head tie. Bressbee was frightened. He kicked out in alarm. BANG! BANG! BANG! The side of the lorry took the brunt of Bressbee's fear but no one came.

"Better get going," said Glyn to the stable lads who had helped load the filly. "The chestnut's started playing up now too. They'll settle once we get moving".

Bressbee travelled from Brighton to Long Mountain with his head painfully tied to the side of the lorry. His head ached and his jaw went numb. The pressure at the base of his neck, from his head being held at an unnatural angle, was unbearable. All he could do to tell anyone was kick the side of the lorry, so kick he did! He kicked all the way down the M23, M25 and the M4. Sadly, the little filly was the only

one to hear him. Glyn had drowned out the noise with the radio and there was no one else around to listen.

It was just getting dark when they arrived at Rob Hughes' yard. The winding lanes from the main route to the yard had extinguished all hope and vigour from Bressbee. Exhausted and in agony from his tether, every twist and turn in the road enforced the pressure on his head and neck. His natural fight or flight response had been triggered. As a result, the moment Glyn dropped the ramp to unload the horses, Bressbee exploded! He kicked! He twisted! He fought to get away from the rope, away from the lorry and away from the person responsible for his torture! He fought for his life! In an almost involuntary fashion, he bucked and thrashed overcome with fury. Glyn watched Bressbee open mouthed. He quickly grabbed the filly and the two of them set swiftly off down the ramp to avoid the rage of the tethered beast.

Silence descended almost as quickly as the wrath had started. Bressbee stood, half hanging, half hobbled, in the lorry. He was spent. The partition that had separated him and the filly was broken beyond repair. Even the metal frame that held it in place was deformed. Glyn returned to the lorry with more than a hint of trepidation. He looked at the sweaty and wide-eyed figure in the lorry and made what he would have described as a 'management decision.'

He spoke to the stable lad at Long Mountain. "He'll never load well in the morning," he spouted. "He's a danger to us all! Let's leave him in here overnight. It'll teach him a lesson for trashing my box. Hopefully he'll relax at some point and realise that travelling isn't so bad. I mean it's not like the lorry'll bite him!" Laughing at his own joke he walked away, leaving Bressbee to his pain and horror for another twelve hours.

Bressbee spent an unimaginable night on the lorry, parked in the yard, hanging by his head with barely the strength to stand. Less than twenty feet away was an empty box, banked with fresh straw that had been prepared ready for his arrival.

****

Clare and James finished evening stable duties and returned to the house for tea, awaiting Bressbee's arrival with great excitement and interest. Through the windows, they could watch the comings and goings at the entrance gates from the comfort of their sofa.

James flicked on the television.

"Spag Bol for tea. It'll be ready in ten minutes," Clare announced as she glanced once again towards the window. 8pm passed without event. Clare and James ate their tea in near silence, occasionally pausing to look out of the window hoping to see a horsebox pull up. 9pm came and went. Then 10pm passed but still no sign of their new training partner. By 10.30pm James was annoyed.

Now in his late 30s, James was born into a military family, raised in Cheshire and educated at Cheltenham Boys. He always was and still is, the archetypal 'Racehorse Trainer'. Never without a cigarette or his flat cap, James Unett is the human equivalent of a Jack Russell Terrier, small, but lethal should you find yourself on the wrong end of his tongue.

"Bloody drivers," he muttered. "Where the hell is he?"

Clare pondered.

"I bet he's stopped at Corley Services and fallen asleep with the horse stood waiting for his tea." She got up, taking the plates through to be washed.

"He'll look like he's run five hard races in a week by the time he gets here if that's what's happened," James retorted. "Don't they realise that the horse is an athlete! Alistair and Miranda will be expecting him to run next week."

"Can't you ring Alistair and find out who he's sent him with?" Clare shouted from the kitchen.

"I've tried but he's not answering. Probably holed up in some swish hotel with Miranda mincing about like Marilyn Monroe," replied James in disgust.

It was past midnight when Clare and James finally retired to bed, morning stables duties would start in only five hours. They slept fitfully, always waiting to be woken by a horse that never arrived.

****

As the sun came up the next morning the stable lads arrived for work at Long Mountain. Glyn was preparing to set off on his journey to Doncaster, to pick up three more horses, when he noticed the lads arrive.

"Oi, Shorty! Feed the horse in the box will you? Might need a drink too," shouted Glyn.

"Mind him though, he's a live wire. Smashed my wagon to bits yesterday! I'll be glad to see him off my hands," shouted Glyn across the yard.

One of the young lads ambled over to the feed room, and then climbed into the back of the lorry with a bucket of water and a scoop of grain. He stopped suddenly and gasped when he saw Bressbee. The horse looked like a rescue case. He rushed forward and untied his head. Clearly he had been tethered far, far too tightly and the horse had been stuck like that for nearly twenty-four hours. As soon as the rope was released Bressbee's head dropped like a lead weight. He hurt all over, completely spent. Bressbee had not one ounce of energy left. The lad offered him a drink, which he sniffed carefully before sticking his nose into the cool, soothing water. After Bressbee had drunk his fill, and being careful not to give him too much in case of colic, the lad offered him the grain. Stroking his neck slowly and tenderly the lad pitied the horse. Bressbee's face hurt too much to eat, the pain of chewing was too much. He chose to go hungry. The lad dressed him over as best he could and placed a fleece travel sheet over his tired and aching bones. Then, with trepidation, he began to tie his head back up again so he could continue his journey to Wolverhampton. As he did so, he whispered quietly to calm and soothe him but Bressbee knew what was coming. He jolted his head up and lashed out, followed by a high pitched whinny full of anguish.

The lad leaped from the lorry like a rat jumping ship. Signalling to Glyn to get moving, they were off. Back down the winding lanes, out onto the main road and onto the motorway for four more long hours.

Clare saw the unfamiliar lorry pull through the gates from her position on the gallops.

"At last," she thought, flinching slightly, already anticipating the dressing down James would give the driver. Working a frisky three year old called Billboa, she pushed him into his last canter of the morning in an effort to get around the track to exit. Billboa skipped along and put in his usual three strides of canter, a shoulder drop and a simultaneous bunny hop just to check Clare was awake. She sat quietly almost unaware of his antics as she rounded the first bend towards the grandstand. Lengthening now, Billboa settled into a rhythmical canter and Clare held him at that pace until they reached the post. Pulling him up level with the paddocks, she skipped off as Billboa walked through to the stables. Handing the reins to Michelle, one of the stable hands, she asked after the lorry.

"Has he unloaded anything Michelle?"

"No, I don't think so," said Michelle. "Do you want me to cool him down and untack him for you?"

"Please," Clare smiled and headed off towards the lorry.

As she neared, she heard a half squealing, half screaming Bressbee, straining to escape his confines inside the box. He had once again found the strength to display his lack of appreciation for the transport arrangements.

Clare dropped the ramp just as Glyn and James rounded the end of the barn. She could overhear them talking.

"He's been like this the whole time. He was sweet at the track and as soon as I loaded that filly he started, got himself in a right state. We left him on board last night. I wasn't risking it. He was mad as a box of frogs in that wagon. I tell you James, that's one determined horse you got there. If you can get him to want to run, he'll win every race he's entered in but he's got a mind of his own. He's a live wire," warned Glyn.

James had been brought up to date on why Bressbee's journey had taken so long and his disdain at the Cavendish's increased tenfold. He wasn't angry with Glyn, but neither did he want him on his yard a second longer, reminding him of his client's ignorance and selfishness.

"Bye Glyn," he said, turning on his heel and entering the barn.

Glyn shrugged and got into the cab, leaving Clare to unload Bressbee alone. Clare quietly stepped up to Bressbee's shoulder. Reaching out she touched him and felt the cold, wet layer of sweat that wrapped him up like a banana skin. He tensed with rage and kicked out again, double barrelling the side of the lorry again and again. Without fuss, Clare undid the partition and unclipped him from the tie ring. Allowing him to turn his head to the outside world and the ramp, Bressbee squinted into the bright sunlight. Clare knew that this was her moment and she used the fact that he was slightly blinded by the sun to get him off the lorry and into his stable in the barn as quickly as possible. Bressbee was home at last.

Chapter Two

15th June 2002

"It was selfish and stupid. You ignorant son of a bitch!"

The words were out there before he could stop them. James immediately regretted them but carried on regardless. "That horse was in pain. He's a living creature for God's sake. He's an athlete! Your athlete! Not a toy to be abandoned on a whim. How do you expect him to eat in this condition, never mind race?"

James paced the office, running his fingers through his wiry hair, desperately trying to control his temper. Stable hands scurried past to the tack room, heads down, getting the jobs done and staying well out of the firing range. James stopped pacing and slumped in his office chair, his gaze falling onto the unfiled bills and receipts. He closed his eyes, pinched the bridge of his nose with his left thumb and forefinger and remembered who paid those bills that lay before him.

"The arrangements were wholly inadequate Alistair. If I am to train this horse for you, I need clear communication. The horse's welfare always comes first! Always!"

Alistair was taken aback. Not many people spoke to him with such honesty or venom. He wasn't quite sure how to react. James released him from his discomfort.

"The horse will be back in work tomorrow. I've checked the fixtures. He'll have his first race on the 26th June. I'm sure we'll see you and Miranda there. Let me know your requirements in plenty of time."

Relieved that James seemed back to normal, Alistair agreed and ended their conversation. James sat in the office, taking his head in his hands. Allowing his anger to overcome him could have cost him and the yard a wealthy client. He was furious with himself. He replaced the telephone receiver with his right hand and reached for the work book with his left. The 26th June wasn't too far off and he needed to sketch out a plan of work for Bressbee to make sure his owners were not disappointed on the day. After all, he couldn't trust himself not to drown Miranda in the nearest champagne ice bucket if she complained about not making the winners' enclosure.

Shielding humidity with the occasional flick of his tail, Bressbee stood in his quarters, fetlock deep in dry, warm bedding with rubber matting cushioning his soles. His head hung low, eyes heavy with fatigue. With effort, Bressbee lifted his head slightly to survey his surroundings. The barn that was to become his home had large internal boxes that lined the walls to the left and right, so that he and his neighbours faced each other. The internal walk way measured approximately two horse lengths in width. He could see a large bay for hay and straw to his left beside a solid door with a lock on it. There were people in this room, taking papers back and forth. He could hear lots of voices. Beside that room he could smell the tack and feed rooms, with the familiar and unmistakeable odours of leather and breakfast. Bressbee could see that his box was numbered 25; it was about five boxes in on the right. His stable was divided from the others by frames of steel, wooden lower walls and metal railings above with the door in the centre of the front of the box. The feed manger was the more modern type, the kind that rotates within the wall allowing for swift and safe feeding practice. He didn't care how his food came to him really, just as long as it came and this type of manger suggested it came frequently. He was pleased. He turned his head slightly to see the rear breezeblock wall painted in the standard form, black to hip height, white above and the two thin wooden windows at the highest point of the rear wall were cloaked in cobwebs and dust as every 'well lived-in' stable window should be.

Bressbee returned his head to its previous position, low and straight. It hurt less this way. He didn't mind the cobwebs, the voices or the coloured paint on his walls. A bed was a bed. And a bed is a panacea to an exhausted horse. After the race, his long and painful journey to

Wales, his torturous night on the lorry and the final painstaking crawl to Dunstall Park, he was worn out.

Clare stood there for some time, just watching him. Aged 28 and ten years James' junior, Clare Jones was born and raised in the Midlands. Meeting the pre-requisite size requirements for a jockey, Clare or 'Jonesy' as James crowned her, weighed in at 8st without trying, and was not an inch taller than 5ft 3in. With auburn hair framing her fine features, brightened by the exercise, she was a lithe athlete in her own sense, mirroring the achievement of the horses in her care. A true horse lover and an accomplished jockey, Clare had no interest in gaining a jockey's licence. For Clare the welfare and education of the horse provided all the satisfaction she needed from her career and her passion was fed at home. Training, schooling, breaking, increasing fitness and riding horses, day in and day out, tirelessly.

Concern and confusion laced her brow. Bressbee was hunched into the corner, his hind quarters wedged in tight for support and his head facing the door. He hung his tired and aching head low, cocked his ears at three and nine and closed his eyes. Clare continued to keep an eye on him as she carried on with the stable duties. He slept all afternoon and well into the evening. Not even the commotion of the evening stables routine could rouse him. Troubled that Bressbee had not as much as scratched an itch all afternoon, and well aware of his lack of interest in his feed, hay or water Clare decided she would leave him to rest until later that evening. Then when all was quiet, she would go and try to engage with him. She had listened to James' furious conversation with Alistair that afternoon and was pleased that she could leave those conversations to him. While he could be briefly overcome with fury, she admired James for his patience and although hard to believe, his tact. When dealing with a client he was largely able to mask his true feelings, able to remain professional and succinct. Although he could quite easily explode, the explosions were short lived and contained. James could deliver his point with the accuracy and deadliness of a sniper. Blunt to the point of astonishment, but charming beyond compare. His private education served him well in that department and he would deliver a verbal blow with the grace and charm of a chorister. They were well matched with their differences. Where James would lash out in fury, she would bury her feelings and respond with care and a practical solution. She had ignored the feelings of disappointment and anger at Bressbee's travel arrangements and focused her efforts on bedding him down and checking on him all afternoon. She knew where her true strengths lay, intuitively knowing what to do to make the horse feel and therefore perform better.

Later that evening, Clare wrapped her jacket around her shoulders as she left the house. Crossing the driveway, she could hear the trip trap of Rascal the Terrier skipping along behind. Never too far from the action, Rascal was Clare's shadow. Black and tan and about ten inches at the shoulder she was a great little ratter. Her short legs and grizzly beard gave away her Jack Russell cross Border Terrier heritage.

"Keep up Rascie." Clare called to the dog who was sauntering along behind. Ignoring Clare she headed straight for the straw pile in search of some sport of her own.

Dusk was just falling at 10pm that June evening, the temperature and the flies had settled down. The occasional shifting of a horse in its box, or the swish of a tail could be heard across the barn but generally all was still and quiet. Clare opened a stable door, his stable door, and quietly stepped inside Bressbee's box. Suddenly a murderous squeaking came from the far side of the barn and Bressbee was jolted from his sleep. Rascal had caught a rat and swiftly dispatched her victim, whilst Bressbee and Clare stood head to head, in the ensuing silence, sizing each other up. Moving round to his near shoulder and taking a less threatening stance, Clare stretched out a hand to stroke him. Bressbee tensed and raised his head, eyes rolling, showing their whites in anxiety as he recoiled into the corner. Sensing his fear and therefore unpredictable response, Clare dropped her hand to her side, turned her shoulders away and lowered her eyes.

"It's OK boy. No need to be afraid of me. I'm here to help you."

She spoke calmly and evenly, showing Bressbee there was nothing to fear. She was aware of her breathing, making sure it was consistent and measured. She stood like that for many minutes, even though it felt far longer. Gradually, she heard Bressbee take a deep inward breath and release it slowly. She felt him relax.

"That's a good boy, a nice deep breath. I'm not here to hurt you, just to look after you."

Curious, he turned his head towards her, probing forward with his nose, sniffing and snorting softly. He smelt the comforting scent of horse. Very slowly, Clare moved towards Bressbee, still not facing him

or looking at him but aiming for his shoulder. Reaching out again, she felt his coat against her fingers. Sweat and grime coated his otherwise gleaming chestnut body. Clare could feel the taut, fitness beneath the skin. This was the kind of tone that only athletes achieve. He was race fit and James was right. Technically he could run on the 26th. Whether he was mentally ready or not was another matter.

Clare continued to run her hands over Bressbee's body, always keeping her breathing and body language at the forefront of her mind. This was not the time to rush.

"Good boy. I'm just checking you over, seeing what I can do to help..." She stopped talking suddenly, her attention focused on Bressbee's legs. She noticed a swelling on the inside of his hocks, on both of his hind legs. Clare knew she needed to inspect this potential injury and treat him immediately. Problematic joints in racehorses can spell the end of a career and Bressbee's career was only in its infancy. Slowing running her hand alongside his flank, Bressbee flickered and twitched swishing his tail and lifting his right hind in a threatening way. Clare remained calm and steady, noticing a family of small superficial cuts on both legs. They were fresh, only a day old at best.

"Now that's strange. How have you done that boy? Some of these are quite deep and they must be sore."

Clarity came to her. He had kicked and cut himself while thrashing and kicking in the lorry. The journey had obviously left physical damage as well as mental.

"We'll sort that out though, don't worry lad. I'm sure they'll heal quite nicely and you never know, you might have some tiny scars to show off to the fillies in the paddock." She joked while she continued to stroke him gently and reassure him with her presence. Mentally she noted to give him some anti-inflammatory powders to relieve any discomfort and aid the healing.

"Silly, silly horse!" She scolded quietly in jest. "Although judging by the state of those legs, you've definitely got some fire in that belly of yours. I wonder how long before you'll tell me how to transfer that fire onto the track?"

Clare, knowing to always leave a session with a horse on a good note, slowly left the stable for the feed room. Adding a couple of veterinary powders to his supper, as well as some warm water to make the meal more appealing, Clare rode the quickest route to a horse's heart – via his stomach. Leaving the feed room, Clare was greeted with a reward for her attention and affection. Bressbee stood with his head over the door watching in the direction she had gone. Clare smiled at him and in return he cocked his head slightly to the left.

"You're a quick learner Mr Bressbee," she noted with pleasure.

She produced her offering of warm sugar beet, chopped carrot, a scoop of mix and an anti-inflammatory painkiller for his hind legs. Bressbee's nose was covered in food before she could even thank him for his patience with her. Clare watched him snatch mouthful after mouthful, then lick the bucket clean. As he washed it down with a long cool drink, Clare smiled to herself and her brow unfurled with relief. She had made a difference and phase one of Bressbee's recoveries had begun. Clare had sacrificed many elements of her life to pursue her passion and what she didn't know about the horses in her care wasn't worth knowing. She was the eyes and ears of the yard, and the voice for the horses. Her steady, calm demeanour allowed her to gain the horses' trust and respect. In return for her dedication, care and commitment to their welfare, they ran and they ran well. Clare just hoped her previous successes would be replicated with Bressbee.

****

16th June 2002
6.45am

"Come on Jonesy. Shift yourself."

Clare looked up from her cup of tea and half eaten piece of toast. Having been up since 5am doing morning stables, Clare was having her first break of the day.

"Bressbee's tacked up and ready to go. What's the plan?" she said, unsurprised by his tone.

James told Clare his thoughts of the night before.

"He's got to stay race fit. I'm not having him wasting away in the box. Is he sound?"

Clare nodded. The cuts were superficial.

"Something's stopping him! He's bred to win in the dirt. I need to know what's wrong. Unfit? Stale? Incapable? Stubborn or unwilling?"

"OK," said Clare through a mouthful of toast. She knew that over the next few exercise sessions it would be her job as jockey to find out

what was stopping him from performing.

Finishing her breakfast and putting her mug and plate in the sink, she made her way to the back door, narrowly avoiding James' affectionate slap on the bottom as she passed him. They shared a smile before accompanying each other to the barn.

The Havana coloured leather race saddle and exercise bridle blended seamlessly into his chestnut coat, both complemented by the vivid green numnah under the saddle. Bressbee looked the part. He stepped out of the stable, a little hesitant but also curious about what lay outside the barn. Ears pricked and eyes bright, Clare was impressed by his eager attitude. Clare gave Michelle her old ride Billboa and as Clare emerged, mounted upon Bressbee, James gave Michelle a leg up onto the little bay gelding. Michelle had been with James and Clare for the past two years. Petite in stature, tall in courage and attitude, she was a valued member of the team. With a history of successful point-to-pointing and the nerve to match any male jockey, she was not only a great rider, but also a confidante and friend to Clare. They had shared many bottles of gin, regaling stories of their past mistakes and glory moments. Clare didn't want anyone but Michelle with her when she was riding a new horse, knowing she would understand her excitement as well as anticipate her decisions.

"Right then Jonesy. One lap of the grass in walk, two in trot and out onto the track at the mile marker," barked James. "Let him walk to start with and get the feel of the track under his hooves. He might test it a bit," he warned. "Kick on to a canter after the first bend and steady away," he said to Clare. "Michelle, if that new one looks like he's flagging, drive him on up the right and get upsides him, give him a bit of encouragement."

The girls nodded and headed out to the track. Billboa skirted sideways at the sight of the drain as they left the yard, and in typical Billboa style, continued to dance along the tarmac to the track entrance. Knowing he had a new rider on board, he fully intended to test her mettle. Bressbee, tense and wound up like a yoyo, trailed behind Billboa. Far too concerned with his surroundings than his jockey, he was bunny hopping and shying at everything and anything that caught his eye. Not having experienced training on an actual course before, as far as Bressbee was concerned he had arrived at the track, ready to compete, to run. Yet he could sense there was something different here. The empty grandstand disconcerted him. The echo of his own hooves on the road was alien to him. For once he could hear himself think. Where were all the people? The horses? The noise? Clare and Michelle rode out through the parade ring, down the walkway and onto the track. They rode straight across it and onto the centre piece of the track, a grassed field.

In years gone by, the grass track that surrounded the exterior of the all-weather had been 'the track' and it had finished right past the grandstand and under the arches. It had also been a jumping track in its day. Now it was fresh turf, manicured and mowed like a croquet lawn. The next loop in was the all-weather surface track and central to that was a road way, for access and the ambulances that drive and follow the jockeys as they race. In the very centre was a field that the resident trainers use for exercising horses. Recognising the wet dewy grass under his hooves, Bressbee tried to stick his head between his legs and bronco along but Clare was quicker than him. Anticipating the move, she held her reins firmly and pushed him forward, not allowing that fatal drop of the head to happen.

Frustrated by her control, Bressbee performed what would become his signature move, bouncing sideways and kicking out with his right hind, with every step forward. His head high and fixed, he looked defiant as he progressed around the field.

"Alright lad, steady now," whispered Clare to the horse. "You'll stretch those legs soon enough."

Keeping the horses in a brisk walk, Clare and Michelle pressed on. This first 10 minutes of exercise was crucial for both horse and rider to warm the muscles and get the blood flow moving through the body. A horse can seriously damage muscle, ligaments and tendons if asked to work without being properly stretched and warmed up first. By the time they reached the grandstand again, both horses were striding out well and Bressbee had settled enough that Clare could feel him stretching.

James sat in the silver Landrover on the edge of the track with the morning's Racing Post and a steaming mug of coffee. As they passed before him, he gave the ritual nod, the trainer's permission to move it up a gear.

Billboa and Bressbee sprang forward into a trot, side by side, mirroring strides they swung along the grass track. After only a few

seconds, the symmetry was shattered. Bressbee's right hind, kick, kick, kicked with each stride, as Clare held him in a trot, not allowing him to speed up as he wanted.

Clare felt quietly excited, trying not to let her anticipation show through the reins to her mount, as the time got nearer to her first canter on Bressbee. James looked quietly on as they rounded the mile corner, trotting on past him again, he could see that Bressbee was not backing off. Clare and Michelle were chatting amongst themselves and they stopped briefly to catch the second nod. James could see Clare had quite a strong hold on the chestnut as they disappeared around the bend.

"One more lap my lad, and we'll see what you think of the all-weather." Clare smiled at Michelle and laughed, as Billboa spooked at the resident tractor and harrows.

"Silly horse has been past that twice already this morning but this time it's going to get him!" Michelle rolled her eyes incredulously and on they rode.

Michelle didn't mind the spooking at all. Envious of Clare's riding ability she had keenly watched and learnt how to ride a spook. Clare would just glide with the horse as if they were one. There was no need for grabbing at the reins or raising the voice. Just a quiet hand and steady voice would bring the horse back into line. Michelle was doing her very best to imitate Clare's riding style, so when Billboa spooked again Michelle kept her hands still and sat back, quietly talking to him, reassuring him that he was OK and that whilst she was riding him he would come to no harm. From a distance, James quietly noted Michelle's developing skills and made a mental note to encourage her to apply for an amateur's licence.

Trying to ease him back from the trot, Bressbee followed Billboa out onto the all-weather surface. So far, so good! Bressbee had been excitable but that wasn't unexpected for a horse in a new environment. Half expecting a show, they weren't at all disappointed. He lunged forward, lurching across the track to the far rail on the right hand side. Bressbee was bolting. With no idea where to, or why, all Clare could do was brace herself for the inevitable fight that would ensue. Bressbee had a hold of the bit and was hanging his head to the left, making it extremely difficult to stop him, or even to go in a straight line. Clare pulled and pulled with all her might to slow him down, but strong as she was, she was no match for him. He had the bit between his teeth and a will to match. Galloping dangerously along the home straight, still clinging to the far rails, Clare stood forward in her stirrups and reached for his bridle to swing him around. Knowing full well that the velocity could ultimately unseat her, she had no choice. It was the only way to stop him from galloping out to the parade ring and onto the concrete road behind. If she had to fall, the softer surface of the all-weather was a much kinder choice. She leant forward, outstretching her fingers, bracing herself for the impact. Just as she was about to take hold, as if he could read her mind, Bressbee straightened his head, released the bit and slowed his pace down to a working canter. Breathing a deep sigh of relief Clare sat back and rode him forward to a trot and then a walk.

Open mouthed, blinking in disbelief, James, who had been about to spring into rescue mode, decided that lighting a cigarette was a far better plan. He watched as the pair passed the bonnet for the fourth time that morning and noticed that Bressbee wasn't carrying a bead of sweat.

"Well ridden Jonesy. I think he likes you!" James chirped from the warm Landrover.

"He'd better like me. If he keeps playing tricks like that, I'll be the only friend in the world he has!"

Hot and sweaty, Michelle and Billboa, who had been left behind rather abruptly, jogged back up the track.

"You alright Clare? I didn't think you'd stop him," panted Michelle.

"I didn't," replied Clare honestly. "He stopped himself."

Michelle looked at the horse with a mixture of fear and awe.

"He's got quite a mind of his own this horse. I think he just wanted to draw a line in the sand. Tell me what he will and won't do. James, we won't be telling him anything, we'll be asking for his permission."

Clare rode back onto the centre piece to cool Bressbee down. Loping along behind, Billboa suddenly looked like the poor relation, paling into insignificance behind the presence of Bressbee. Taking one stride forward in walk and then a side step and right hind kick, one stride forward, a side step and a right hind kick...

Troubled by this morning's antics, James started the engine and returned to the yard to set the next two horses up for exercise. If there was one thing he knew, it was that keen and fast did not make a

winning racehorse. Consistency and self-motivation were the ingredients needed to be a good horse. With that thought in mind he wondered what training methods they would need to employ to get the best from this horse, because Glyn was right. If they could get him to want to win, nothing would beat him.

Chapter Three

16th June 2002

Clare untacked Bressbee in his box. After removing his saddle and bridle, she began her usual post-exercise routine to check for any damage, bruises or cuts. She spoke softly to Bressbee as she firmly, yet gently, ran her hands over his body.

"Thanks for the challenging ride Bressbee. You're not going to make my life easy now are you?"

Bressbee stood still, slightly turning his head towards Clare's rhythmical voice.

"I can't keep calling you Bressbee though, it's far too formal. What would you like me to call you?"

Again, Bressbee replied with silence, yet this time with a slight swish of the tail. Clare continued to run her hands down his limbs, concentrating on the joints, checking for puffiness or heat. She noticed the cuts on his legs from his journey to Dunstall Park and was pleased to see that they were healing nicely.

"How about Buzz? Will Buzz do? Short, to the point, and when you're carting me off somewhere, it's easy to shout at you."

This time Bressbee nudged her softly in the ribs. She took that as a sign of acceptance of his new stable name. Buzz it was.

Content with his condition following exercise, Clare made her way to the house and switched her mind to more pressing matters, how to cure Buzz of his dangerous and ineffective racing habits. The bottom line was that Bressbee had a job to do, just like every other racehorse. A racehorse must run and be successful enough to satisfy the owners' requirements. In return they are housed in 5-star accommodation, fed high quality feed, bathed, groomed and kept fit and healthy. They also receive the most advanced veterinary care, access to a swimming pool and have a monthly pedicure. It's a lifestyle that most people could only dream of.

Clare knew that James and her were willing to broker a deal with Bressbee and were able to pool their combined knowledge and experience to help the horse. Getting a tune from a horse is a skill. It cannot be learned from a book or a college course. It is something that must be lived, breathed, experienced and loved, learning through the journey. But the newly christened 'Buzz' would have to make his end of the deal work too. Clare was worried about his attitude, not to mention his desire to bolt and veer to the side. Clare opened the back door, her mind whirring full of possible solutions to their dilemma.

"Alright?" James greeted her.

"He's settled. No after effects," Clare responded, walking to the fridge to prepare lunch.

"Stubborn beast," James retorted. Clare smiled at his abrupt manner. She knew he would also be thinking of ways to improve Buzz's performance, despite his dismissive turn of phrase.

"I prefer Buzz," started Clare. "Stubborn beast doesn't have the same ring to it. Buzz is short, to the point and easy to shout during exercise. He's Buzz from now on at home."

James shrugged his shoulders glibly. He'd have preferred a much ruder name than that.

Clare placed two plates of chicken salad on the table and took her seat on James' left hand side.

"How about a brush bit rubber?" She questioned. This small circular piece of rubber would be inserted between the bit and Buzz's cheek. The brush material would be glued to the inside of the rubber, touching Buzz's cheek if he pulled or leant towards it. The unfamiliar sensation of the brush would make Buzz move away from it, therefore encouraging him to run in a straight line.

"It's a start," James agreed. "But it won't stop the bolting and won't stop him rushing to the far rail."

Running wide means running further, and if Buzz was running a longer route around the track, to win he'd either have to be considerably fitter or considerably faster than his competitors. James remembered an occasion when he worked in Italy, where a young colt in training repeatedly ran wide. The trainer under which James worked as an assistant, made the horse exercise around the track in the opposite direction, therefore changing the scenery and making the horse think before bolting off. James knew that the majority of tracks in the UK run anti-clockwise, Dunstall Park included. It would also mean if Bressbee bolted left on a clockwise track he would learn to run with the rails on his left, conditioning him to run that way.

"Buzz will train clockwise, learn to hug the rails," he told Clare. "Dig out those brush bit rubbers, we'll need them too."

Clare didn't need to question James' decision. She knew he'd have thought it through. She nodded, agreeing through mouthfuls of chicken salad.

****

17th June 2002

7am

Putting yesterday's disastrous training behind them, Clare and Buzz together with Michelle aboard Billboa, headed out onto the gallops. Today was a Tuesday and according to James' training schedule, Tuesdays meant that there would be two canters. Clare was curious to see how the new training methods would work. Buzz was wearing his brush bit rubber and together with the clockwise canters, Clare felt confident that Buzz would not play the same trick as yesterday. The only downside would be the inability to check his running times against the previous day's performance. The weather had taken a turn for the worse and rain was bouncing off the ground, making visibility poor. Clare could barely see Buzz's ears in front of her. The difference in the wet surface would also make Buzz's times slower in comparison. Yet, she hoped it might also discourage him from bolting into the horizontal rain. As he jogged onto the field in the centre of the track, Clare recognised Buzz's step, skip, kick routine from the day before. She smiled, as the routine felt rhythmical in its discomfort. The waterproof exercise sheets, placed over the horses' backs to protect them from the rain, were proving to be useless. Buzz's was soaking

wet and clinging to his haunches like a wet suit. After the second trot, Clare reached back and pulled it off. The less reasons she gave Buzz for his behaviour, the better. Michelle followed her lead and removed Billboa's too. The girls looked at each other and smiled, both realising there was no point in trying to talk to each other today. The wind and rain made it impossible. Looking bedraggled and nothing like elegant athletes, Buzz and Billboa made their way to the track for their canter.

As she emerged through the rails onto the track, Clare glanced down at the brush bit ring, wondering if it would do as she intended. Buzz tensed, ready to plunge forward. Immediately he was surprised by the aid to turn right, clockwise, instead of left, anti-clockwise around the track. His desire to bolt had been temporarily foiled by James' plan. Clare took advantage of his surprise, bridged her reins and nodded to Michelle, signalling her intent to move into a canter. With that they were off. Automatically, Clare felt Buzz take hold. Propelled by the driving rain behind them, he leant on the bit, using his brute strength to disempower her. She smiled at his tenaciousness, knowing that she and James were a step ahead. As he had done the day before, he tried to lurch right but was stifled by the rail. Determined not to be put off, Clare felt Buzz veer left instead, bringing the bit brush into effect. This surprised him and encouraged him back to the rail. Clare rewarded him by gently slowing him down to a trot having completed a decent piece of work. Despite his best attempts, he had hugged the rail like a winner.

Clare sensed that allowing Buzz to process what had just happened would not benefit either of them. Without giving him time to devise another escape route, she turned him around, now riding anticlockwise round the track. Pushing the trot forward, she urged him past the pre parade ring and back towards the stands. Once again, bridging her reins she nodded to Michelle. Receiving a positive response, Clare rode on, steady away with the rails on her left. Bressbee dug in, working forwards into the bridle and into the driving rain, they disappeared down the track and out of James' sight. Michelle and Billboa rattled on after them. The kick back from the track was bad, especially in the rain and Michelle slowed Billboa down to get out of range from the flying debris shooting from Buzz's flying hooves. Immediately Clare knew that this run would be different. Her body covered in goose pimples as she felt the power that sets a talented horse apart from the herd. She knew it was only meant to be a 'canter' but her intuition took over and she rode Buzz on relentless and insistent she drove him forward like they were racing in the last furlong of the Derby. She had ridden him round the entire 1 mile track, working him on the left, in a straight line, hugging the rail. The rain stung her face, the wind thundered in her ears. Her hair came loose from its tie and stuck to her neck, just as Buzz's mane was plastered to his. Mud decorated her teeth as she grinned like a schoolgirl. This was the beginning of a promising team, her and Buzz. They were experiencing this together.

From his position in the Landrover James could not see the other side of the track, and although encouraged by Buzz's run clockwise, James wasn't sure they'd be so lucky this way round the track. He had noticed on the clockwise run that Buzz had a high rolling knee action, slightly out of character for a modern flat racehorse, yet on the polytrack surface, his high action seemed to serve him well. He had run cleanly. Watching with anticipation, James kept his eyes on the final bend of the track, where he would see Clare come back into view through the rain. With relief, they appeared. James realised his mouth was open with surprise as, despite the torrential rain, he witnessed the pace that Buzz was working. He could feel the vibrations through the Landrover as his hooves battered the track tirelessly. Clare was crouched low and still, like a cat poised for the kill, as they crossed the finish line. James realised he had been holding his breath. He exhaled slowly and purposefully, not taking his eye off the chestnut horse for a second. Struck with admiration for Clare and the raw ability of the horse, James smiled, knowing that the gauntlet had been laid. Buzz had shown them his cards.

In the driving rain that summer morning, he had given them a glimpse of his talent and oh boy, did he have talent.

With nine days to go until his first race, James, encouraged and quite frankly enlightened by Buzz's performance, put the horse on the yard work plan. The work plan for all the horses on the yard followed a strict pattern;

Monday: One canter
Tuesday: Two canters
Wednesday: Two canters; the second, a strong 'working' canter
Thursday: Roadwork and a nibble of grass
Friday: One canter

Saturday: Two canters; the second, a strong 'working' canter

Sunday: Day off

On the days that Buzz had two canters, he was worked in the same way as before, his first was clockwise, the second anti-clockwise. For the next ten days Bressbee was worked solely by Clare. She began to realise that his jog, skip, kick routine was every bit as standard as the work plan for the yard. Yet frustratingly, after his one morning of promise and talent, he was not consistent. Quirky and unpredictable, if the mood took him, he could produce amazing results. Yet he could equally go out onto the track and be spectacularly average.

New horse, new owners, James needed Buzz to put in a good performance in his opening race for them. It was good for business. James, fully aware of his heightened anxiety in the build-up to a race, was unable to hide his frustration after Buzz produced another mediocre performance on the track.

"That bloody horse Jonesy! Is it going to run like a greyhound or trot out of the stalls like a donkey?"

"God only knows James. He's got a mind of his own," Clare retaliated, frustration gripping her. She knew what he was capable of but couldn't find the key to unlocking Buzz's desire to win.

She looked down at the horse beneath her, who hadn't even broken a sweat in training,

"He can do it. I'm sure he'll pull it out of the bag. He's just settling in, testing and seeing what he can get away with. Leave him to me."

"That's just it. I can't. He's not the only one on the yard. Christ Clare I know you like a challenge. It's heart-warming, it really is. But what have you achieved with him?" James challenged unfairly.

"There's other horses here too that need your attention, ones that will appreciate it. You've dropped Billboa like a stone and Steve will be here to watch him run next Wednesday," he sniped, knowing this would hit a nerve.

Clare's face darkened. She looked up at James and in a measured tone gave him the facts he needed.

"Billboa is working perfectly well for Michelle. Steve can watch her work him. I'm not racing him. You've booked Eddie to ride him on Wednesday, so it makes no difference if I'm training him or not," she told James directly. "As for Buzz, we've got to get inside his head. You may not understand, but he needs to like me James, to trust me, to respect me. He is a horse that won't be told, only asked politely. I appreciate that this is an approach that you are completely unfamiliar with, but you aren't right all the time!" Jumping down off the horse, she grabbed the reins and strode purposefully towards the barn, Buzz jogging obediently behind her.

James shook his head and watched her walk away. He needed a drink. Rascal was hovering beside him angling for scraps. He turned and walked to the Landrover as Rascal skipped after him and jumped into the front seat. A shared packet of pork scratchings would have to do.

****

26th June 2002

He had been drawn third. Starting from the third starting gate from the rails meant he wouldn't have too much track to make up to get to the rail, the shortest route to the finishing post. Horses that are drawn with a wide draw have further to run, so a low draw is more favourable. Clare knew the art of riding out from the starting gates would come into play here. The jockey would have to ride well here to ensure a good position. Although, over a mile there is opportunity to make up ground and position, every good jockey knows a forward start and a good clean break out the stalls, sets up the race, whether it is over a five furlong sprint or a mile.

The jockey in question was Shane O'Neil. He was an experienced jockey who had won some big races. James had followed his career and his stats and he had been seen riding for the likes of Richard Hannon. He rode flat horses, which would stand him in good stead for the ride on Buzz. Clare knew he would need to be strong and have versatility. He would also need the experience to deal with Buzz's broncing and kicking, his leaning and hanging, his bolting and skipping. Often jockeys will ride several races in a day, sometimes at different race meets across the country. Each race only lasts a few seconds or minutes, depending on whether it is a flat or jump race. Unless the jockey has ridden the horse on a previous occasion and is familiar with him, he would have on average, ten minutes to listen to hints and tips from the trainer and possibly a few words of warning from the stable lad, before jumping on the horse for the start of the

race. May the best man win! Trainers choose horses, train horses, choose races suitable for the horses they have trained and then they choose a jockey. Once on board and across the track, it is out of the trainer's hands. He has to trust that the jockey can ride the horse to the best of the horse's ability and obtain the precious win. Like sending your child to school for the first time, all the trainer can do is let go and watch from a distance. In James' case the 'distance' is the Owners and Trainers bar, getting a scotch to steady the nerves.

Clare looked at the race card. Bressbee's name was there, plain to see. He was entered and declared to run in the 'Ladbrokes, Place Bet Here, Handicap' for three year olds and above, running over a distance of 1 mile and half a furlong on the track at Dunstall Park. It was the third race of the evening, starting at 6.50pm. The prize money for first place was £2,968, second place paid out £848 and third place £424. In addition, there was the usual £100 prize money for the best turned out horse, the horse that looked every inch, 'The Racehorse.'

Clare knew the trip wouldn't cause him an issue. He'd been cantering the mile with ease for the last week barely breaking a sweat, but then he'd barely been trying in Clare's opinion. More than capable of winning this race, he had been given a 'rating' of 62. The higher the rating the better the horse is deemed to be and partly on this basis 'favourites' are determined by the bookies. Entered against horses rated 58, 59 and 60, Buzz should have been the favourite, but due to his lacklustre performances of late he was sitting at 10-1. Not bad, but certainly nothing to write home about and that was the story of Buzz's entire career to date; nothing to write home about.

Clare could hear the race day fever building from inside the sanctuary of the barn. The steady rumble of the horse boxes filling the lorry park, hummed in the background as the car park started to fill with staff cars. As the vehicles entered the front gates, they still had to drive through the dips, in force since the outbreak of foot and mouth the previous year. Clare recognised the sound of the splashing, as the front and then the rear wheels of the vehicles were disinfected as they drove through.

The horses too could sense the change in atmosphere and this was the downside to being the resident at the track. On race days, the horses knew what the commotion and bustling meant. This made them tense, anticipating action. Clare and the stable staff always had a longer than normal routine, as the mucking out and exercising was laced with, "Stand still!" or "Steady lad!" Then the occasional, "Bloody hell! Stop knocking over the barrow!" To help muffle the sounds from outside world and calm the horses Clare would turn the radio up a notch or two.

Afternoons were generally the quiet time when the horses would sleep, but not on race day. Every horse on the yard would be wide awake, listening to the unfamiliar whinnies of visiting horses and the huge increase of traffic and people buzzing about Dunstall Park.

Buzz had been dressed over. Polished and plaited, he looked formidable. Not a pretty, lightweight thoroughbred, he had bone, substance and width. The horse was a powerhouse in terms of his physique. Although impressive, Clare knew that his athleticism wouldn't win him this race, his attitude would. She still had no idea what frame of mind he was in before being ridden out, and as she painted oil on his hooves, making his hooves shine like wet pebbles on the beach, she tried her best to sense if tonight would be a celebration or not.

"Come on boy, give me a hint...?" She begged Buzz.

He continued to stand looking out of the stable, ears pricked, focused on the noise outside the barn. Clare realised she was going to get nothing from him while he was so distracted. Hanging on the rack, his racing bridle was gleaming and polished ready for his debut run. Clare heard the commentary for the 6.25pm race. It was time to take him out to the paddock.

****

James met with Alistair and Miranda and safely installed them in a private box in the Owners and Trainers lounge. As they opened a bottle of Dom Perignon to wash down their hors d'oeuvres, James shook his head slowly and made his way down the stands to the weighing in room. Here he found Shane stripped down to his racing tights just about to get on the scales.

"Alright lad?" Muttered James. "Journey OK?"

Shane had ridden two at Kempton that afternoon and after a hellish stint on the M6, due to an over turned lorry, he had a banging headache.

"Not really. That M6 is a shite road, over a shite city. Frigging depressing! And Dolan was in the back whinging about his ribs after falling at Doncaster last Tuesday. Christ he's a tart that one," Shane complained. James raised his brows in response.

"But I'm here now. Instructions?" Shane asked, while walking to the scales. Carrying his race saddle he was beckoned by the steward to climb on. He was a lean lad, narrow framed with mousey brown, tousled hair. He reminded James of a young 'whipper-in' on the Gloucestershire hunt he had ridden with as a lad. Balls of steel that whipper-in had and Shane was no different. Gaining his racing stripes on the back of a hard apprenticeship in Ireland, he had ridden out his claim by the time he was twenty four.

"Bressbee. He's fit and strong. A quirky bugger. Watch for him leaning and trying to hang right. Jump him out and kick on."

Shane looked a little despondent. He was hoping for a winner to round off his day.

"He has bags of ability though, if he can be arsed to work," James concluded. Shane cracked a smile and took that as a challenge.

Briefing over, James disappeared. It took a lot to startle Shane O'Neil, but that was exactly what happened when he arrived in the ring. James had just managed to secure Bressbee's saddle as the horse fly bucked, his hind feet narrowly missing the young girl who was leading the horse behind them. James reeled back, stumbling slightly from the powerful shove the horse had given him. Clare hung on to the front end, firmly gripping Bressbee's reins to stop him from bolting off. Step, skip, kick went Bressbee as he circled the ring, demonstrating his signature move for all to see. Shane raised his eyebrows as he pulled on his hat.

"Quirky, you said James, not bloody demented," he half-joked. "Come on leg me up, let's get this over with."

Shane pinged into the saddle and slipped his feet into the irons. Like a seasoned skier through slalom gates, he moved effortlessly with Bressbee as the horse continued to prance and dance for the occasion. He looked magnificent, markedly bigger and more impressive than the others in the ring, grabbing the attention of the crowd. He held his head high, determination shone from his eyes. Bressbee's colours were red, green and yellow. The silk arms were canary yellow, set against a grassy green body. Red patches over the shoulder matched the bright red silk of the Shane's riding hat. The silks were vibrant, and bright, just like the horse. Shane relished every minute of the showing aspect of racing. He also loved the female attention it was rewarding him with. As Bressbee plunged around the ring for the final time, he spotted the young blonde steward he'd ended up bedding after the last race meet here. He allowed his mind to wander briefly, questioning if she'd forgiven him for not returning any of her calls? It was a good night, one he wouldn't mind repeating.

The arrival at the entrance to the track brought his mind back to the matter in hand. Clare slipped the lead rein free and with a gentle pat on Bressbee's tense neck, she watched him spring forward. Turning left in front of the stands, the riders and their horses would canter to the three quarter mark and then turn back for a second canter, as the start for the mile was on the far right of the track. This was Clare's favourite part of the race process. In sharp contrast to the manic rush for the finish, here she could watch the beauty and grace of the horses as they moved, flowing and swinging effortlessly like shooting stars across the sky. She noticed the subtleties of each horse adjusting to its environment, their eyes and ears flickering as they weighed up their new riders, steadily working through the aids and commands. First walking, then trotting and finally cantering down the track. She admired their courage as they accepted their new jockeys without question, just as the jockeys accepted their new mounts. Fascinated by their compliance to their instructions, these were all the reasons Clare herself was never inclined to apply for a jockey's licence. Inspired by educating the horse, understanding the individual animal, building the bond between horse and rider, she believed that the strongest bonds between man and his mount were formed over time, not in the parade ring in front of the baying, but paying crowds. Clare wished that she and James had enough paying owners for them to employ their own resident jockey. Someone she could work alongside, ride alongside and teach. Teach to ride from the heart with feeling, ride with the horse, not just on top of it.

Abruptly disturbed from her reverie, she saw Bressbee immediately try to pull right to the far rail as he entered the track. Shane hauled him left and sent him on, balancing quietly atop the horse that was bucking and kicking in what can only be described as bloody-mindedness and frustration at being foiled by his jockey. Shane turned him at the marker and followed another chestnut back down the track. Bressbee

settled into a flat, dull canter, thudding compliantly and pulling up level with the parade ring ready to walk the last furlong towards the stalls.

Clare knew from that one canter, that after all the anticipation and hype of the morning, Bressbee was working like a donkey. She sank inside, knowing that his performance would be at best a placing. Not wanting to watch him put in a poor effort, she turned away, wishing she could disappear off back to the barn to hide. Instead she stood wondering just what she could do to understand Bressbee, and discover what motivated him to run. She had to watch him, to learn from him, no matter how demoralising it was to her. It was important to them both that Clare was there for Buzz when the race finished, handling him, giving him reassurance, providing a familiar face and routine, while Shane went to un-tack and weigh in again.

****

James made his way to join Alistair and Miranda for a drink during the race. He would have to be back on trackside immediately after the race, but he needed a drink after saddling that horse. Also, after his phone call with Alistair the other day, James knew he had to make up for his lack of self-restraint and colourful language, no matter what he thought of the man.

To James, Alistair Haden Cavendish was, quite simply, a pompous inflated man. An entrepreneurial businessman in his earlier years, he now owned a large corporate hospitality and events company. His first wife, June, had been left alone far too often, as his business regularly called him away. After fifteen solitary years, she finally met someone else and filed for divorce. Alistair was devastated, although his tough exterior never betrayed this fact. The following two years were swallowed by an extremely expensive and messy divorce that outwardly made him bitter, inwardly fuelled his guilt and ultimately was responsible for his complete lack of confidence. Clearly seeking personal gratification from pleasing his second wife Miranda, he would bow to her every command. What Miranda Cavendish wanted, Miranda Cavendish got.

Privileged, yet uncouth and brash, Miranda never had to contemplate working for a living. Educated at a private girls' school in Surrey and sent to finishing school for two years to 'mature', Miranda mixed in circles that afforded her the luxuries and opportunities that she was now accustomed to. It was these very circles that led her to Alistair, a divorcee on the rebound. He was ripe for the manipulation that ensued. Ensnared by her perfectly sculpted body, angelic face and onyx black hair, he was like a lamb to the slaughter. The parties and social melee that she had dreamed of were finally hers, week in and week out. After the partying waned, domestic bliss set in and Miranda settled for a life of beauty therapy and coffee with the girls. She had a personal trainer, a soft top BMW and an account at Selfridges. Miranda was set to cruise through life blissfully obnoxious and disliked and having a racehorse was the cherry on top!"

Just as Miranda loved the lifestyle, Alistair loved the kudos he gained from being able to waltz into the Owners and Trainers lounge with his young wife on his arm. Wining and dining his clients at the country's best courses was a weekly ritual for Alistair which ended abruptly when his last horse, a strapping 16.2hh blood red bay called Ali's Demon, was over-raced, leading to his tendon giving way. On Alistair's orders, Ali's Demon was quickly and mercilessly shot. That same day, Alistair approached James to scout another horse, something that would put him in the winners' enclosure on a weekly basis and not break down.

As James entered the lounge, he could hear Miranda loudly discussing Ali's Demon's euthanasia with another owner's wife.

"It was obviously the trainer's fault. The horse was unfit to race. It's not like we forced them to race it," she remembered wrongly.

"Alistair bought me another straight away. It was simply wonderful of him. I have so missed going to the races," Miranda crowed.

James arrived at Miranda's side, clutching his whisky a little too tightly, the whites of his knuckles betraying his anger and discomfort. The other owner took James' arrival as her cue to leave and escaped quickly. Miranda carried on like a woodpecker on a tree.

"Verity and Robert will be pleased. We were due to meet them last weekend in Berkshire after the Polo, but there was nothing suitable to invite them to because we weren't racing our own horse."

Alistair interrupted her monologue. "Thank goodness! Robert's one hell of a bore! All he did was prattle on about forward selling, buying back and the strength of the Euro against the Pound. It was enough to

make my brain dribble out of my ears!" Alistair guffawed at his own joke, oblivious to everyone else's silence. He often found Miranda's friends arrogant and immature, full of the vigour and gusto that he once could lay claim to, but no longer. Sometimes it all got the better of him and he longed for the quiet life he once had with June, the walks they went on with their old retriever, the simple dinners for two in the Hertfordshire cottage they had lived in.

Miranda, for all her rudeness, was intuitive. She sensed Alistair's longing and taunted him, just loud enough, for the entire lounge to hear. "What's the matter old man? Can't keep up?"

She knew he was still in love with June. She also knew he did not have the mental strength to do anything about it. Yet just knowing he yearned for her, was enough to drive Miranda mad with jealousy.

"The new horse is chunky and ginger," announced Miranda, to no one in particular. "Just like Alistair's ex-wife!" She screamed with laughter at her own joke, before adding for good measure,

"Just think of the pleasure I'll get when the jockey whips and whips it!" Miranda cheered and raised her hands in triumph, ready to accept the applause which never came.

James noticed Alistair visibly wilt.

"Very witty sweetheart," he replied with a withering smile.

Eager to change the subject, yet mindful of his manners, James brought Alistair's and Miranda's attention to the track.

"They're loading the last of the horses now. We'll be off shortly," he reported.

Suitably distracted, Alistair and Miranda turned to watch through the huge glass windows on the front of the lounge. From there they could see the mile starter, positioned to the left of the stands, the horses would pass the crowds at the beginning of the race and then race around the track and back along the home straight in front of the stands to the finish line. They could just make out some commotion behind the stalls. The last horse to load was showing some spirit in his refusal to enter the stall.

"Isn't Bressbee drawn third James?" Asked Alistair.

James squinted, looking hard, trying to pick out the number on the numnah of the chestnut horse refusing to load. He could see the cherry red hat and yellow arms.

Number 3, it was Bressbee.

There were three stall handlers behind pushing him and one in front fruitlessly pulling him. The handler to his right skilfully dodged his right hind as he thrashed and kicked. Out came the blindfold which they pulled swiftly down over his head and together with an almighty shove, Bressbee went in. From the comfort of the lounge, James, Alistair and Miranda watched Shane lean forward and pull off the blindfold in one, skilful movement, preparing Bressbee for the start. Within a split second the stall doors sprang open and they were off. James held his breath, willing Shane to get him out and on the rail, tucked in and working straight.

Shane just had time to bridge his reins once more, after removing the blindfold, before the gates opened. Bressbee surged forward, his powerful stride carrying him across the ground a crucial amount further and faster than his competitors. He immediately hung right again as James had warned, but Shane was ready for him and held firm pushing him into position on the rail. He got there a length ahead of the leading group. Travelling well and settling into his stride he galloped, loping along effortlessly on the track he knew. Shane sat quietly with Bressbee in the lead, expertly giving and retaking the reins with the horse's movement, as they made their way down the back straight, Bressbee still leading the field now by almost two lengths.

At this point in a 1 mile race, a jockey would want to hold his ground, ready to push for home on the final bend. Yet a jockey alone cannot make the horse perform in that way. The horse can be trained and educated, cajoled and encouraged, whipped and bullied, but if he doesn't want to give that little bit more, he won't. And neither will he win. Horses have free will, just like the rest of us. Clare's prediction on Buzz's attitude that day was spot on. The horse remained static, loping along, doing his job in his usual disinterested way. Still leading out of the last bend, Shane asked for more speed and was met with a serious lack of response. Rowing along, Shane bounced, pushed, kicked, shouted and finally whipped him, all to no avail. Bressbee cantered over the line having been passed by three horses on the home straight.

In the lounge, James' concentration on the race was interrupted by Miranda's hellcat screaming as Bressbee led from the stalls and round the track. Yet her shrieks of encouragement soon gave way to insults at the jockey, when they finished fourth. James spotted the static pace

from Bressbee after the last turn, and knowing he would never make it home in the lead if he didn't notch it up that crucial gear, he gave up watching and settled for full commentary from Miranda, as did the rest of the lounge.

He downed his drink at the bar as the horses passed the finish post and hastened past Alistair and Miranda, hoping they wouldn't notice his quick departure. Lady Luck was not on his side. As he walked through the door onto the terrace, he heard Miranda's unmistakable tone. "Come Alistair, we're going with James to see what's wrong with the horse and that incompetent jockey."

James bit his tongue. Today, he was determined to be civil.

Clare was exasperated, but not surprised by Buzz's performance. She had ridden him in spirit from the parade ring, feeling herself tense and push forward, as though she was on board herself. Through the last bend she willed and mentally pleaded with Buzz to show the crowd what he was capable of. When she saw Shane raise the whip, she knew it was over. It just wasn't the way with him. In a very short time Clare had realised that attempting to make Buzz do anything was a non-starter. You had to ask, and anything other than a polite request would switch him off. She wondered how many times she would have to tell people that before they listened to her.

Buzz trotted friskily back to the parade ring, having barely broken a sweat, but with a very out of breath and puffing Shane on board, shaking his head and cursing him quietly.

"We had that in the bag. It was ours. He's a pig that horse. He wouldn't give me an inch, sour sod!" Shane slipped off nimbly and undid the saddle. Dragging it off Buzz's back on tip toes, he turned on his heels and stormed off to the weigh-in room. Passing the three triumphant horses in the winners' enclosure, he swore loudly as he went.

Clare looked across to the stands to see James making his way over. She continued to walk the parade ring with Buzz in hand, cooling him down and letting his body and his muscles settle after the race. James walked over to the water troughs and returned with a bucket and a sponge. Cooling him off, he relished what he knew would only be a moment's silence before Miranda and Alistair cornered them.

"James, I do hope you're going to dress down that jockey. Our horse was galloping home marvellously until he stopped riding him. He may as well have got off him. Bressbee would have finished better by himself!" All too soon, Miranda was standing behind James with her hands on her hips, demanding action. Alistair arrived behind is wife, slightly out of breath from trying to keep up with her.

"Miranda, the horse ran well. First time here with a crowd. He worked well, on the rail and straight. We couldn't have asked for more," James lied. He knew that Buzz only needed to give a little bit back and he'd easily have won the race. He had made the ground at the start. James met Clare's eyes as they placed Buzz's rug across his back. He could see that she agreed with him.

"Well I think it's that blasted jockey!" Miranda remained defiant, looking for someone to blame. She marched towards Buzz, displaying her anger in every step. Startling him as she reached out to pat his head right between the eyes, he leapt back afraid the anger would be directed at him. His sudden movement caused Miranda to jump backwards, straight into the water bucket James had been using. Squealing in shock she leapt up, embarrassment and dismay painted all over her reddening face.

"Oh my goodness! Miranda, here let me help you. Oh dear, urmm, let's get you changed quickly. Bressbee scared you," said Alistair with concern, and a desire to get her out of the parade ring where she was making quite a spectacle of herself. Humbled and covered in dirty water, Miranda was escorted by her husband to the restrooms.

Clare could not help but smile.

"God pays bets without money," she chuckled to James, while patting Buzz on the neck to calm him down. "I'll walk him over to the barn James. Is Shane OK?"

"Here he is," replied James, returning Clare's smile and nodding to their jockey who was striding towards them with a grim face and an envelope in his hand.

"Best turned out! Here you go Clare. The only thing this pig'll win I'll wager," Shane snapped grumpily. Not feeling comfortable when taking praise for her efforts, Clare stuffed the £100 in her pocket and made her way with Buzz to the barn. Shane, meantime, shook James' hand and strode off. Having finished for the evening he headed back inside to the bar in search of that young blonde.

Chapter 4

Mornings involved grumbling staff, hordes of paperwork, a barn full of fresh horses and declarations for races across the coming week. James had just ended a call from a jockey's agent, organising a pilot for, 'Fight the Feeling.' He looked like a promising horse and James had planned a run for the following week. He was taking Buzz to Southwell for his first race away, later that day, and decided to take five and have a coffee and a roll up before the inevitable trials and tribulations of the day began.

Summer had finally arrived and the morning was bright and crisp like the horses James could see striding across to the gallops. As he supped on his Espresso, Michelle passed the office window riding one of the two year olds in training. James smiled as he recognised his training bridle on the horse. Willy Lonergon had given it to him in the Adelaide Spinal Unit after his fall.

That fall, thought James, that summer! Relaxing back into his chair, he took a drag on his roll up and drifted back to the summer of 1982. After leaving the Army, in a less than honourable fashion, he was given a ticket to Australia by his father. The idea was, that during this year of travel, James would, 'grow up!' James embarked on his new adventure with the same gusto as he applied to the rest of his life.

Flying into Sydney he checked into the Park Hotel. It was a four storey building with the lower two floors providing hostel type accommodation for travellers and students. The upper two floors were home to the 'local working girls.' It was the perfect combination for a hormonal single guy who had been sent to the other side of the world to 'grow up.' James was in his element and he certainly gained a copious amount of experience during his stay! Despite the all fun he needed to find a way to finance the $40 dollar a week rent for his grubby little shoebox.

Being a grafter, James was happy to turn his hand to anything. As a result, it wasn't long before he started at A1 Car Rentals, washing cars by day. By night, he washed dishes in Kings Cross, Sydney's red light district. Typically for James he got itchy feet. After all, Australia was a huge place! He saved his earnings and bought himself some transport. It came in the form of a Honda 500 motorbike, an ex-traffic police bike. James planned to travel around and see some of the country. He already had a contact, through his father, in Adelaide called Willy Lonergon. Willy trained flat horses at the Genalta Stud, nestled in the hills behind Adelaide. Wasting no time, James jumped on his latest ride and headed that way.

James grinned to himself as he remembered rocking up the drive at Genalta and introducing himself to Willy, who was an Irish horseman through and through. Willy gave James a handyman position, mowing lawns and painting railings and James cracked on with his work in typical Unett fashion. From his throne atop the mower, he watched the strapping thoroughbreds grazing in the paddocks and working on the gallops. He wondered what it felt like to ride a racehorse, to be the best, the fastest, the winner?

Willy Lonergon wasn't just intuitive with horses, he could see James was keen and asking all the right questions, so he offered him a ride.

"Ah! Sure, you're the right size and weight for riding and too small for painting guttering and anyways, I've no ladders long enough! Can you ride lad?"

"Of course I can ride!" James lied through his teeth!

Ride was a complete stretch. Sit on perhaps, but ride a prize winning thoroughbred racehorse, no chance!

Still, that was how James Unett sat on his first racehorse, in the hills in Adelaide, the capital of South Australia. He lasted a grand total of three days. Then on the third day he fell, resulting in a crushed, fractured vertebrae and a three week stint in the Adelaide Spinal Unit. It was there that Willy Lonergon gave him the bridle that Michelle was using.

James' recovery was relatively swift. The three weeks he spent strapped to a spinal board served its purpose and after being advised to, 'take it easy' for three months, James returned to the stud and to limited stable duties. However, the inevitable had happened. Whilst 'doing his time' in the spinal unit, James' mind had been filled with thoughts of horses. He was awestruck and spellbound by their power and strength. Although small in stature, James Unett is a formidable character with a competitive edge. Not much gets the better of him, in mind or in body! However that horse had! Not only had it tossed him aside like a rag doll, it thought nothing of it. The gelding had turned on its heels, given James a dismissive buck in defiance and cantered back to the yard, tail high and ears pricked. That kind of behaviour generally got James' attention, and boy did it grab his attention this time. For three full weeks he thought of nothing but riding techniques. In his mind's eye he dissected every mental image he could conjure up of jockeys' riding styles. Where the hands were held, how the legs were used like spring boards, where the balance came from, how they stayed atop those horses, skipping and bucking out to the gallops? James Unett planned to find out for himself, and not just find out, but perfect, and master the technique. He dreamed of harnessing that power for himself and winning with it. Winning at home, now wouldn't that be a head turner!

James watched, listened and learned every aspect of running a successful stud. From the most effective method of loading a barrow full of muck, to the horsemanship used to back a yearling. He soaked it up like a sponge. He was busy, always helping, always there as the spare pair of hands, prepared to offer his assistance to watch and listen some more. True to form it wasn't long before James decided he had gained all he could from Willy's yard, combined with the urge to discover more of Australia, he moved on to Vernon Brockman's yard in Perth. Here, they prepared yearlings for the sales. Vernon specialised in flat racehorses and James at this point was well enough to start riding again. A clean slate in a new yard, he bluffed his way back into the saddle. Still extremely wooden at this stage, James was useless! However, the months spent scrutinising other jockeys had paid off and the way he learned to use his own body was vastly improved. Now he needed to learn how to feel the horse, anticipate his moves and his thoughts. Despite his accident, James was fearless. Where many riders would have been put off for life, after a fall of that seriousness, James was bloody minded about the whole job. He rode every horse he could, to gain the invaluable experience that comes with hopping on and off of several horses a day. James learned to go with the horse's movement rather than brace against it. He learned to push a dancing horse forward, not back off from it in self-defence. He learned the value of soft hands and a strong seat and legs. He learned to ride.

Once again, it wasn't long before the road called to James and he set off on his Honda towards the famous 100 mile beach. North lay Darwin and Cairns, however the road beyond became the notorious Bull Dust tracks. Completely unsuitable for his bike and tyre type, James was forced to turn back. Although his employment paid well in terms of knowledge, James was existing living hand to mouth. A set of off road tyres was completely out of his budget. So, after some sightseeing and partying, he headed back to Willy in Adelaide, where he remained until his year was up.

James returned to the UK for a short stop, and a short stop it was! The camaraderie in the yards he had worked wasn't dissimilar to that of the Army and James could feel the pull that everyone who lives for horses has felt before him, that feeling of discontentment when you're not around them. The boredom and hours you have to fill when you don't have to go back to the yard for evening stables. James had caught the bug. Life without horses didn't step up to the mark. This made him stop, take stock and work through his options. He wanted to be around horses, lots of them. He wanted to race. He wanted opportunity, coupled with freedom. For James, the two words freedom and UK didn't feature in the same sentence. Hence, James found himself travelling to Critiquette Head's yard in Chantilly to ask for a job. She had 180 horses in training and according to James' calculations she must need a hand with the mucking out! Scoring a job on the basis he must be serious, if he was prepared to travel across Europe on a hunch, he worked there for six months as a stable lad, again focusing on riding and producing horses fit for the track. There were many differing methods employed by trainers, and the differences between Australia and Europe were vast. Feed types, bedding used, tack, bits and even the climate, all play significant roles in the training of the horses and James to some extent had to revisit some of his methods and techniques accordingly.

Within the staff ranks, James was taking some flak. The lads and lasses simply could not understand why an English lad, with Newmarket, the epicentre of the horse racing world on his doorstep, would be abroad working! They jibed he was rubbish, couldn't ride and would be laughed off any serious training yard. Never one to be proven wrong though, it wasn't long before James was back in the UK, in Newmarket, working for David Morley. Not just as a stable lad either, he had gained the title, 'pupil assistant'. This basically meant that he was a 'dogsbody' with a title! James was quietly smug about his achievement and thought it was a great one in the eye for the staff back at Head's yard!

In 1989 after a couple of moves within Newmarket, James became assistant trainer to John Hills in Lambourne. It was during his time with John that James flourished and truly spread his wings. He loved the job and fondly recalled those days as the best of his life. The horses, the women and the beer were the perfect cocktail for James. With John, he travelled and raced worldwide, going to France, Sweden, America, Hong Kong, Italy and St. Moritz.

In Sweden with Glide Path, they won the Group 3 Stockholm Cup.

Docksider, who was a fabulously talented bay gelding and one of James' personal favourites, took them to America where he was 3rd in the Breeder's Cup, then on to Hong Kong, chasing glory in the Hong Kong Mile.

In 1994 entrusted with 13 horses, they travelled to Italy to race. James used every bit of his experience to date, coping with how international travel and changing climate conditions impacted on his horses and staff alike. Ordered and methodical, he ran his side of the operation smoothly and professionally, ensuring all those in his care received the individual attention required. James knew his horses, inside and out, and they got what they needed to keep them content and willing. Willing and longing, to run for him and win.

Night Flyer was the horse that shaped all. In February 1999 the four year old bay gelding, rated in the early 80s, was entered to run in St. Moritz, Switzerland. The races in St. Moritz were run in the month of February, on a snow surface, underneath which was a frozen lake. Preparing a horse to run under those conditions was virtually impossible in the UK and so Night Flyer and James were sent to run an early race, two weeks ahead of the intended race on the 21st, to see how the horse coped.

Night Flyer ran on the 7th but finished at the back of the field, 7 out of 10. He blew up almost immediately after coming out of the stalls but although he lost the chance of winning, James felt the horse had done well considering the surface was all new to him. Night Flyer's jockey, Newnes, said that the horse had held himself back. James had a gut feeling, that with some training and time, Night Flyer could improve and perhaps even have a chance in the bigger race in two weeks' time.

James, who by this point had firmly learnt to trust his gut with a horse, rang John Hills back in the UK and shamelessly told a pack of lies. He told John that the horse had run extremely well, and that he was impressed by the run. He insisted he stayed with the horse for the fortnight, until the next race, to train and educate Night Flyer on the snow. Reluctantly John agreed, and James was delighted. He had just finagled a two week skiing holiday!

For the next fortnight James' routine involved him getting up, exercising and training Night Flyer every morning, spending the afternoons on the pistes and his evenings on the piss! James was in heaven. The lifestyle in St. Moritz was James Unett to a T!

As the fortnight passed, Night Flyer steadily improved, staying the course and gaining confidence on the alien surface he was expected to trust and gallop flat out on. James firmly believed he would be in with a shout. Back in the UK however, John had read a write up on Night Flyer's first race and it didn't match the glowing report filed by James! A little miffed at being so easily duped, he grudgingly allowed James to continue, as bringing the pair home now would be a complete waste of time and money. He decided he may as well sit it out and run the horse. Night Flyer did not let them down. On the 21st, he ran again in the listed Grand Prix Hermes, with Newnes on board. Finishing 3rd out of 16 runners, a pleasing result, and a greatly improved performance over such a short time. James never stopped admiring the thoroughbred for its intelligence and learning ability. They were truly versatile creatures.

Ever the analyst, James formed the conclusion that to do well in St. Moritz, you needed a horse not only with ability but with a tough mental attitude. One that could cope with the arduous journey, the alien landscape and the crisp, crunchy snow surface that was the stage on which they were expected to perform. You also needed a front runner,

a horse that could lead the race and stay there, because the kick back from hooves during the race was horrendous. Snow flies everywhere, into everyone's eyes, stinging, burning and disorientating for both horse and jockey. The prize money was fantastic and placing in the race itself a real accolade. Certainly not the 'run of the mill' grass or all-weather track primped and preened by grounds men. Racing on the ice was, in James' view, the ultimate, where trust and belief between horse and rider was intrinsic to success. The horse needed the courage and mental fortitude of a cavalry horse steaming into battle. To win at St. Moritz you needed a horse as bloody minded as James Unett.....

His mind wandered back to the transport guy who had delivered Bressbee. Glyn had said that the horse was so bloody minded, that if Bressbee himself decided he would win, nothing would stop him. James pondered that thought. Perhaps Bressbee had it, that X factor. Did he really have those vital ingredients needed to produce glory on the ice? He had that front running attitude, and when he fancied he was tough, mentally and physically, and he was bred for the dirt tracks of the USA.

Although not exactly snowy, more akin to it than grass! For a second, James could see that gleaming chestnut coat, glowing against the snow, as Bressbee cut across the ice like a swan on a lake.

"Get your gear now, and get off my yard! How DAAARE you treat him like that," screamed Clare in a strangled tone.

James was jolted from his chair, dropping his roll up. He muttered, stamped it out and went out into the barn to find out what all the commotion was about.

One of the stable lads was scuttling like a wounded crab across to the tack room, presumably to 'get his gear' before hot footing it, as quickly as possible and as far as possible from Clare as he could possibly get! Meantime, she was running back out of the barn towards the car park. James followed suit, but as he rounded the corner of the barn he collided with Bressbee. Loose and black with sweat, the horse was panicked. Buzz sent James spinning round as he headed back to the sanctuary of his box.

James was stunned. One minute he had been reminiscing about the fun he'd had in St. Moritz and the next he had been run over by Buzz and found himself sitting in a bedraggled heap outside the barn! He looked up to see Clare, fleetingly acknowledge his predicament, en route to her far more pressing issue, Buzz.

Slick with sweat and blowing hard, Buzz was standing in his box with his head in the corner, just as tense and psyched as he had been on that first day. He was due to race at Southwell that afternoon and while Clare was working on the gallop, one of the lads had decided to take it upon himself to load Buzz ready for James. Big mistake!

Buzz had taken one look at the wagon, ramp down, ready for the off, and refused to take another step. Not wanting to lose face, the lad enlisted help in the form of a broom. He had pushed and shoved and pulled and yanked, clattering Buzz's back end, trying to bully and bludgeon him on. The broom was no match for Buzz. He recoiled, spinning, twisting and turning away, going anywhere but forwards onto the lorry. As far as Buzz was concerned, that lorry meant pain. He could vividly remember his head, forced into position by the rope tied too tightly, and then the hours and hours of relentless agony he had been subjected to. He wasn't daft and he wasn't about to give in! He would rather have died fighting, than let them put him back in there.

Clare had finished on the gallop and was crossing back to the barn, when sounds of the drama first reached her ears. As she came into view, Buzz was standing on his hind legs, rearing dangerously above the ramp, the whites of his eyes showing as they rolled in fear. The lad had given up with the broom and had tied a lunge rope from one side of the lorry, around Buzz's hind legs and held the remaining end in his hand. Every time he applied pressure, the horse went up. Buzz couldn't move left, couldn't move right, couldn't go back and wouldn't go forwards. For him, the only option left was up.

Leaping off and chucking her reins to Michelle, Clare dashed across the car park. But she was too late. The lad, startled by Clare's arrival, dropped the rope and Buzz, seizing the opportunity, bolted. He crashed through the gates and across the car park, ropes flailing around his legs. It was all Clare could do to stop herself from strangling the lad, who had started back to the barn. She followed him to get a lead rope and some help to catch Buzz, before he slipped or tripped on the rope. It was at this point James had heard the commotion and emerged from the office.

In his blind panic, Buzz's natural instinct was find safety and no sooner did he reach the car park that he realised his safe warm stable was in fact in the opposite direction. Turning back for home, the rope

tangled in his legs, panicking him even more. He flew through the gates for a second time and headed back to the barn. Just at that moment, James had come out from the entrance and met with him on the corner! Insignificant to Buzz, whose base instinct was to get back to his box, he barged past James intent on reaching his sanctuary.

Clare quietly slipped in behind Buzz. Despite her rage, she drew a deep breath. She knew Buzz would sense her anger and panic even more. Horses are intuitive beyond our comprehension and she knew he would read her vibes as anger towards him. Nothing could have been further from the truth. Reaching out for him, intent on removing the 20 metre lunge line that was wrapped around his legs, she felt him quiver. His flanks heaved in and out, like sheets blowing on a washing line. He was all in, dripping and black with sweat. She talked soothingly, in hushed tones as she worked. Slowly and steadily she unclipped the rope from his head collar, so that he wouldn't panic, step on the rope and tighten it around his head. Then she unravelled the rest, winding it through his front and back legs as gently as possible, trying not to stress him further. She knew the risk of colic would be high. A twisted gut can be fatal in horses and he was a prime candidate for it in that state.

James hobbled across the yard, took one look at the horse and went in search of a sweat rug. Buzz needed to dry out and keep warm. Although the horse was sweating hard, if left to dry without the rug he would likely catch a severe chill. Handing it to Clare, he muttered he would have to go and withdraw him from the race. There would be no way he would be running at Southwell after that! Deflated, James always worried when a horse was a bad loader or traveller. Racehorses have to travel to races. Simple! If they don't or they find it stressful, they are just expending energy best saved for the race itself.

Clare had rugged him and the steam rising from his body hung in the air like smoke. The heat was almost tangible. Even James could feel it, as it radiated from inside the box. Wiping his face and neck and gently, Clare could feel his breathing relax and gradually return to normal. Calming him was her first priority, sacking the lad her second. She operated a zero tolerance policy for that kind of horse handling. The lad would have done well to have vacated Dunstall Park permanently before Clare's work with Buzz was done. He was quiet now, and she offered him a cool drink. Not too much, only the half bucket. If he drank the full bucket, the cold water hitting his stomach in large quantities could well be another reason for him to colic. He drank his half and looked brighter. Lifting his head to her hands for a fuss, she knew he'd be OK. He was badly shaken and very hot, but he was a tough horse. He'd come right again. She just needed to get her thinking cap on, around ways to get him past his loading and travelling phobia. She would need to work with him, and fast. Buzz was in full time employment and had a job to do. Alistair and Miranda had employed him to win races and not just races at Dunstall Park.

Safe in the knowledge that Clare would take care of Buzz's immediate needs, James walked back towards the office to withdraw him from the race. It occurred to him that he would also have to call Alistair and Miranda. He slumped back into the chair knowing that that would be the worst call of all. They would have no concern for Buzz. They couldn't care less how he arrived at the race, as long as he won. Besides, James felt they were partly to blame. If they'd arranged appropriate transport when they bought him in Brighton, he wouldn't have had the long and painful journey that he did and he wouldn't have such an issue with travelling now. James sighed. It was never the training of the horses that was the problem, it was always the people. Be it unreasonable owners, or inexperienced stable lads, it was always the people who caused the grief. That horse would now have serious issues with travelling. Issues they would have to work very hard to overcome. Such issues take time, and time is money. Frowning and mocking himself, he lifted the receiver to make the first call.

"To think I thought for a minute there, we could get him to St. Moritz!" He said out loud as he dialled the numbers.

Chapter 5

"That's it my Buzzer boy, nice and easy now lad," Clare coaxed Buzz forward onto the ramp. It was the fourth day of Clare's one on one training with him to help him overcome his phobia of loading. Clare had decided that taking Buzz straight from the stable and presenting him with loading would only end in tears. By nature he would jog, jump and kick in anticipation. He mostly behaved liked a coiled spring, ready to explode at any minute. Whether ridden or in hand he would arch his neck, jog on the spot, and to the rider or handler, would feel a good six inches taller and wider than he really was! Clare felt this had been Buzz's downfall to date. His excitement and anticipation had been misread in Clare's eyes. Clare felt no fear or concern for herself when she was around Buzz; she knew his springy impatient manner was his coping mechanism. It was how he dealt with his own emotion. From a training perspective horses do one of two things. They internalise their feelings, withdrawing, becoming quiet and submissive or they externalise them and display it in a very physical obvious manner. Clare preferred the latter. At least you knew what you were dealing with; you could read it, assess it and deal with it accordingly.

Clare felt Buzz had been viewed as a problematic horse. Some racing yards train many horses. Those horses need to be compliant and they need to do their job with the minimum of fuss, so staff and trainers alike can crack on with the next horse, because in racing there is always the next horse. Some yards were very much more 'factory line' than Clare and James' yard, as Clare knew all too well. Having worked in Epsom some years earlier, Clare had seen first-hand the misunderstandings that can occur between horse and handler. These misunderstandings usually ended with the horse being blamed and punished for its actions. Whether with a harsh tone, louder voice or with the whip, Clare had seen it all across her career. It saddened her that within the industry there were self-proclaimed professionals who had not a clue how to read a horse. Professionals, who were seemingly unable to tell the difference between fear and defiance and ability and indifference, the result being that the spirit and beauty of the horse, the star of that very same show, would be lost in the process. Sometimes forever, but not Buzz! She had decided as much after that first gallop. Not my Buzz.

It was with these factors in mind that she started work on him. It was Clare and Clare ONLY that now dealt with Buzz and she decided she would spend no more than five minutes at the end of each exercise session working on the loading issues. In theory he should have released a fair bit of energy on the gallops, which should help to settle him down. Bringing him straight from the box would have been fruitless. He was always far too hyped and wired to communicate clearly with him. Clare decided she would let him have his playtime and then ask him to listen to her way of thinking once they were at the loading ramp.

At Dunstall Park to assist with loading the horses, there was a raised concrete walkway higher than the ground level. This walkway was built to be as high as the average lorry base, meaning the loading ramp to the lorry could be lowered onto the end of it, allowing the ramp to lay flat rather than steep and uninviting to the horse. This would assist Buzz and his re-training on loading. It would make the lorry a less frightening place for him to enter.

On the first day of his loading training, Clare simply walked him up to the ramp, turned him round and walked him back to the barn. She could feel his tension build as they approached the lorry.

Ears pricked and head high, he snorted in disgust at the mere thought of it all. However when she turned him away and led him back to the barn Buzz was surprised. He looked quizzically at Clare as though asking what the point of that was. Clare was thrilled. He had done 100% of what had been asked. She asked him to walk up to the lorry, and when SHE decided to, they walked back to the barn.

The second day was the same, except Clare asked him to stand still, just for a second before she turned back for the barn. Again she could feel resistance from Buzz, but he wasn't sure what she would ask of him next, so he stayed listening, alert for Clare's instruction.

Day three and this time Clare led him to the lorry and stood him by the side of it, away from the ramp. Buzz was starting to enjoy this game! He didn't like that lorry, but he wasn't sure what was happening next and curiosity was getting the better of him. Buzz was very bright and picked things up extremely quickly. Clare knew if she got it right he would load no problem. That day she tied him to the side of the lorry, and picked his feet out, untacked him after his exercise and then walked him back to the barn. He froze, panicked by her tying him to the side, but he was outside and he knew he could get away. Clare spoke soothing quiet words as she stood by his head stroking his neck.

"There, there lad. Quietly now, no bother lad. Nothing bad here Buzz."

He stood tense but understanding and although not completely at ease, he accepted it and trusted her.

On day four Clare knew she had to tackle the ramp itself. Walking him to it, she never faltered and stepped briskly onto the rubber ramp. For a second Buzz, blindly followed, but only for a second. He stopped in an instant, fixed and firm. Clare had to get one more step forward from him. It was crucial, otherwise in Buzz's mind HE had made the decision to stop at that point, and the decision making HAD to be Clare's domain. She stood on his left, level with his head, lead rope slack in her left hand with her right hand caressing his neck. She wouldn't pull or push, shove or shout. He had to take that step forward because he trusted her. It had to come from him. His eyes darted left and right looking for alternatives, his ears turned to the side, listening to her voice, calm and quiet like always. His weight was on his front legs, his right hind, the one he always kicked with was resting on its hoof, twitching. Just one more step.... He lurched forward suddenly and made that vital move. Clare timed her instruction perfectly. She called him, applied gentle pressure and turned him off the ramp and back to the barn. Success at last! After all the miles that horse had galloped on exercise, that one small step would prove to be the most significant step in his career.

Clare was thrilled and Buzz was completely confused. The important point was that he had done as he was asked without a fight, and without pushing the point she ended her training on that positive note. However small that step was, the end result would be massive in comparison.

By day ten Buzz would walk up the ramp and put his head into the lorry, before turning back for the barn, but today was the day he would have to go right in. Clare planned to walk him straight onto the ramp and in, then immediately off again. She marched positively towards the lorry, striding onto the ramp Buzz by her side. She kept going, one step, two steps, three steps and they were in. He had done it. He walked straight in, without as much as a blink. She turned on her heels to the left, Buzz following her body language like a riding school pony following the tail in front. She waltzed off the ramp grinning like a cat with the cream and skipped back to the barn.

From the canteen, James had a great view of the track, car park and loading area. He had seen Clare working with Buzz and he had seen him load for her. He never interfered when she was working, he knew better than that. He knew she would crack his fear, and that it was just a matter of time and patience, both of which Jonesy had in abundance when it came to educating horses. He sighed with relief when the horse walked in. He had entered him for a race the following weekend at Haydock. Fight the Feeling was running there too, later that same day, so he would have a companion to travel with which should help settle him. He hadn't mentioned it to Clare, deciding not to pressurise her with the loading issue. After what he had just witnessed, it was about time she knew, so he downed his coffee and made his way out to the barn.

"Saturday the 9th!" She exclaimed. "Fight the Feeling is running there too, and Tigress runs here that same day! Bloody hell James no pressure!" Clare shook her head with a wry smile creeping across her lips. She whispered to Buzz, "Piece of cake buster, piece of cake."

Clare's training continued. She had progressed to having him stand in the lorry for ten seconds and then getting him off again. Next she tied him inside, picked his feet out and untacked him inside before taking him back to the barn. She then had James shut her in with him for a few minutes, and the next day she was shut in with him with the engine running. Slowly, slowly catch a monkey! It was working. He was visibly relaxing more and more each day, to the extent that when they had finished their exercise on the gallops, he would start to walk towards the loading ramp without being encouraged to do so. Finally, on August 7th, two days before the Haydock meeting, Clare drove him round the car park at Dunstall Park in the lorry. She could hear him kicking, but she knew that was just Buzz, kick, kick, kick! She unloaded him after just two laps of the car park and he was none the worse for it. Perhaps a little befuddled as to why he had been driven round the car park when he could have been back in his box munching on hay, but certainly not stressed by the experience.

Saturday 9th arrived and what a busy day lay ahead. James was running Tigress, a dark bay, three year old filly at Dunstall Park that afternoon. He also had Clare taking Fight the Feeling and Buzz to Haydock for the meet there. Both geldings were running over the mile, Buzz first and Fight the Feeling in the following race. James planned to saddle and lead up Tigress at Dunstall Park and then travel with Fight the Feelings' owners to Haydock to catch the latter race. He wouldn't make it in time to watch Buzz run. He wasn't overly bothered though, he had artfully managed to avoid Alistair and Miranda.

Clare was busying around the yard, preparing racing tack, jockey silks and the horses for the journey. Fight the Feeling would load first and Buzz second to give Buzz the reassurance of another horse, but not so that he felt trapped between the other horse and the outside world. Clare was desperate for him to load and travel well. She didn't care if he ran well on that particular occasion, what was important was his mental state upon arrival. She knew all too well that if Buzz found the outbound journey stressful, reloading to come home would be impossible and they would be stuck at Haydock.

Looking at Fight the Feeling standing in the lorry, Buzz shuffled into the box and turned left ready to be tied. He was keeping his eye on the gelding and his ear on Clare. He loved her steady rhythmical tone, constantly peppering his ears and he had learned to zone into it and relax. He was doing that now, concentrating hard on Clare, her every move analysed and anticipated. Checking his head collar was properly tied and he was comfortable, she left him and lifted the ramp, still talking to him as the ramp closed and the bolts slide across. "Piece of cake, it's a piece of cake my lad…" she called as she walked to the driver's door. Hoisting her tiny frame up into the lorry she waved to James as she prepared to leave. She could hear him… Buzz… kick, kick, kick!

Pulling out onto to the M54 and planning on joining the M6 to travel to Haydock, she was immediately diverted. An accident on the M6 had closed the motorway and the traffic was being diverted up the A49 towards Whitchurch. Irritated by the thought of taking the lorry down a far more winding route, Clare pressed on keeping her driving as smooth possible.

When travelling in a lorry or trailer, the horse experiences something similar to standing up travelling on a train. That swaying feeling and rocking motion as the train speeds up and slows down is the most physically challenging part for the horse, as it also is for humans on a train. Clare was so intent on keeping her braking smooth for Buzz that she took a wrong turn at Whitchurch. To make matters worse it had started to rain and the sky in front of her was black. Climbing a bank, the road got higher and windier the further she went. Eventually, she pulled over in a car park. They were way off course and had arrived at a Candle Factory near Beeston in Cheshire!

No sooner had she pulled over when her mobile phone rang. Flashing intently on the screen, James' name blinked at her. She answered, barely able to hear him above the background noise but learned that Tigress had come 3rd in her race at Dunstall Park. Heartened by the news, and refusing to allow the awful weather and the ticking clock to get the better of her, Clare headed back down the hill in search of the M6. She had an hour at best to get the horses to the track.

Eventually Clare turned onto the leafy avenue that was the entrance to Haydock Racecourse. Lined with horse chestnut trees bearing their spikey fruits, the grand entrance was a welcome sight after the awful journey they had had. Against the dreary sky, the vibrant greenery of the trees was easy on the eye after the grey monotony of the motorway. Sploshing through a huge puddle in the gateway into the lorry park, Clare felt as bedraggled as the car park attendant looked. The rain was lashing down. Parking the lorry as close to the entrance as she could manage, Clare turned off the engine and sighed with relief. They had arrived in one piece.

Kick, kick, kick, sounded the reminder from the back of the lorry! Clare jumped out dragging her coat with her. She wanted to get him off as quickly as possible, to give him time to settle before the race. Dropping the ramp, she started talking to him, naturally flowing, it

was rambled, jumbled nonsense about candle factories and rain, but to Buzz it was a tonic, his favourite kind and he lapped it up. Whickering to her as she untied him, she checked him; he was warm, but not too hot. Pulling his rug over him so as not to expose his warmed muscles to the cold driving rain, she unloaded him and took him straight to the race day stabling. Settling him, she returned for Fight the Feeling or "George", as he was known to his friends, a tall but slender horse, bright chestnut, with a huge white blaze down his face. George was sent to James to be trained as a three year old colt. However during that time he suffered intermittent lameness issues and after some discussion was returned to the owner to be gelded and rested until he was brought back into work as a four year old. George was keen and genuine and James hoped he would run well on the grass track at Haydock. George's owners were particular favourites of James'. They were down to earth, straight talking horse folk. James knew that kind of owner didn't come along often!

Haydock is a Grade 1 track, which essentially means it's classed as a good quality venue. Capable of holding significant numbers, in terms of spectators and horses, it is a grass track and they host on average 33 race meets per year. Based in vast woodland, it is one of the premier tracks in the UK. Prize money at such a track made it well worth the visit, winners stood to earn in the region of £3,000-£4,000. Clare looked along the saddling boxes across to the course and could see the race goers shrouded in raincoats and mackintoshes in a sea of multi-coloured umbrellas of every shade and design you could imagine. They bobbed around like apples in a bucket as their owners hustled and jostled for the best vantage point of the track.

Matthew Henry was booked to ride both Buzz and Fight the Feeling, in the Wilmslow Handicap and the Stanley Racing Handicap respectively. Clare settled the horses and went off in search of him. She wanted to ask how the track was holding up in such heavy rain. She also needed to deliver James' instructions regarding how to ride the horses during the races and to hand in the colour bag with silks. Dodging the raindrops, she stood on the wooden veranda of the weighing in room when she spotted Matthew. Sheltering from the downpour, he was leaning against the wooden rails, drying his hair with a hand towel.

"Hi Clare, I didn't recognise you in your drowned rat costume!"

Matthew Henry was a well-known face to both Clare and James. Cheeky and funny, he rode alongside James in America. Whilst working Docksider prior to the Breeders Cup, James considered him a friend and a great young pilot. A well raised and accordingly mannered boy, his parents had encouraged his riding for many years and supported him in pony racing throughout his teens.

He had ridden in an earlier race and was taking a break. Discarding the towel, he proceeded to light a cigarette. Clare quizzed him on the going.

"What's it cutting up like out there?"

"Kick back's pretty bad, and it's sloppy. If it keeps up like this they'll do well to grow webbed feet!"

"Great, just what we needed!" Clare muttered sarcastically. "I'm going back to the yard. See you in the ring." In her hurry to get back to Buzz, Clare had almost forgotten to give Matthew his instructions.

"Hang on little lady! What are my instructions for Buzz!?!" He chuckled after her.

Wheeling round, raising her eyebrows at herself she began.

"Settle into the stalls and make the break as clean as you can, don't rough him up or he'll fight you all the way. Watch him, he'll hang right. He's a natural front runner so send him home, but don't hit him; he can do it without that."

With that she was off, back to her Buzz. Matthew stamped out his cigarette but on looking up he groaned, as he could see Alistair Cavendish and his irritating wife heading in his direction. He had already been accosted earlier in the afternoon and subjected to Buzz's owners' 'riding instructions' for the horse. Jockey's often had to smile sweetly and suffer ill-informed and indignant owners. That said, Matthew knew it all came with the territory but today he could not stand listening to Miranda moan about her wet hair yet again, so he dived into the weighing in room and took cover.

8pm

"Steady lad, I know you like to give them a show, but steady lad. Not that I care what they think but they are looking at you like you're mental!" She hummed the words into his cocked ear as he snorted and stamped around the ring. Buzz was ready to rock and roll.

"Leg me up then Jonesy!" Called Matthew and with that he artfully dodged one of Buzz's well-timed kicks. She threw him on. Getting the

nod from the stewards she started for the track. Neck arched, tail flying, Buzz's coat shimmered in the rain. Clare had a feeling, one she barely dared to acknowledge. He had loaded well, travelled well and danced like a ballerina for the crowds. Could he win for her next?

The lead rein loosened and he flipped onto the track like a copper coin. Buzz's bronze coat radiated against the green of the track. He looked every inch the athlete but Matthew didn't truly feel the horse was listening. He was co-operating, but he wasn't totally tuned in. He decided to follow Clare's advice and not interfere with him too much. It felt like the horse knew his job and that he was going to do it regardless! Drawn number 1 he was in the stall on the rails. There were 14 horses in the race, Apache Point the favourite. The rain was relentless, drumming down hard with the sky dark and gloomy above them. Matthew could feel the rain running down his back, the sleeves on his silks stuck to his skin like a wetsuit and his fingers were like ice blocks formed and fixed around the rubber reins. It was supposed to be summer!

8.10pm

Clare stared hard through the rain at the grass track which spread in front of her like a sea of green. The turf reminded Clare of velvet. It looked perfect and lush but she knew it would be wet, deep and slippery. The stalls for races over a mile, were positioned across the track to the far right. The horses would race out, down the back left, around the corner and down the home straight in front of the spectators to the finishing line. Clare watched the stalls spring open, on the huge screens positioned centrally so the punters could see every inch of the action. For a nano second she held her breath but suddenly there he was, visible only because he was on the inside. He had made a clean break and although he wasn't leading, he was chasing them down. Clare mentally urged Matthew to get him out of the kick back and get his head clear so he could run home. Travelling well down the back straight Buzz was gaining and Matthew needed to pull him off the rail to the right in order to get round and past the leaders. As though Buzz read his mind, when they rounded the final bend he made his move. As the runners fanned out across the track, Matthew held Buzz along the middle line. He knew the track would be less churned up there and Buzz would be able to gallop more freely. Mud was flying everywhere. The horses were plastered and the jockeys were barely able to see through their goggles. Buzz then stepped it up. His high knee action made it easy for him to plough through the field, cutting across the turf and gaining headway. He ran on making his bid for the win. As he edged towards the stands, giving the crowd and their bobbing umbrellas an eye full of his magnificent torso, he motored home. He led well over the last 2 furlongs and was ridden clear of the group for the last furlong, passing both Apache Point and Route Sixty Six, he won by a clear 3 lengths. Clare could barely contain herself. She knew he would do it, she knew he could do it, and she knew he would and could if he wanted to!

The winners' enclosure at Haydock is a pretty ring, with mature trees sprouting up providing a canopy for the occupants. Claiming his well-earned position at the 'first' post Buzz, was subjected to the hooting and screeching that went along with a win for Miranda. Standing close enough for the photographer's benefit, but with enough distance to prevent any mud transfer from Buzz, she made herself the focal point of the enclosure. She squeezed Matthew's bottom as he went to weigh in, and as he turned in shock to find out who the perpetrator was, she winked wickedly at him. He laughed out loud at her. Clare was so enthralled by Buzz and his win that she missed half of the goings on, but nothing would have surprised her regarding Miranda. The woman was a menace. Alistair stood resolutely for the pictures and in a timely fashion gathered up his trollop and exited stage left back to the bar. Clare threw Buzz's rug across his steaming back and left the enclosure. She would need to cool him down properly, despite the rain, get him a drink and she must speak to James. Fishing through her pockets for her phone, she made the call.

"James, he did it.! He bloody won!" Breathless, Clare babbled down the phone like a child on Christmas morning.

"I know we were listening on the radio. Is he ok? Did he come out of it alright?" asked James.

"He's fine. Wet and muddy but fine. Listen I've got to go. George is in the paddock. Where are you? You guys had better hurry or you will miss the race!" Not waiting for a reply she hung up and turned to wash down Buzz. He was thick with mud. The well groomed and glossy looking horse he had been, less than 20 minutes ago, looked like he'd ploughed a field! Clare did not care one jot. He was her Buzz, with or without mud and with or without winning!

From the race day stabling, she could hear the commentary for the 8.40 race. A local trainer, who had attended the meet that day, offered Clare a hand with saddling and leading up Fight the Feeling. The two races, the 8.10 and the 8.40, were back to back, and as competent as she was even she couldn't be in two places at once! As Fight the Feeling was a more straight forward horse, and because she was by this time hopelessly biased, Clare opted to lead up Buzz and let the lad take Fight the Feeling. As he had also been drawn number 1, so his stall would be on the rail. It was a smaller field than Buzz's race with only six entrants in this one. Buzz and Clare stood completely still in the stable, straining their hearing to capture every word of the commentary.

"And they're off... Fight the Feeling has missed the break. Matthew Henry will have to make all to recover from that mistake. East Cape leads in the pink and Up in Flames is sitting pretty as they come down the back straight. Pension Fund is on the outside, while Hard Lines and Princes Prospect are battling along. Fight the Feeling is gaining now and as they take the first corner, it looks like Fight the Feeling has beaten Princes Prospect into 6th. Into the second corner and they are travelling now. Here he comes, Fight the Feeling has closed the gap on East Cape and Up in Flames, who both look like they are going backwards. As they head into the home straight, Fight the Feeling is running wide. Now he's got his head in front, leading and it's Fight the Feeling, followed by East Cape and Up in Flames. Fight the Feeling is leading by 2 ½ lengths, there'll be no stopping him now! And it's Fight the Feeling first! East Cape second! Up in Flames third! A double for James Unett and Matthew Henry today!"

Clare was stunned, they'd won the double! James' first double as a Trainer! By this point, oblivious to the world around him, Buzz was grateful for the wash and fresh rug. He was content, he was a racehorse, he'd been to the races and he'd won. Job done! She was all too aware he had won £4,032 in prize money too. That would keep him in feed for a while!

Leaving Buzz for a second, she stepped outside the stable to see George being led off the track into the paddock. She could see his proud and jubilant owners in the paddock; with what she was sure was a huge bottle of champagne. Through the mud she could just decipher Matthew Henry's smile and the whites of his eyes. James was stood off to the left, never too fussed over the cameras. Clare knew he would want to check George's legs and then slope off to the bar.

"They did it!" She exclaimed to James as he led the spent gelding back into his box.

"What a cracking day! Tigress and now the double here! Fantastic! How'd Buzz run? I didn't see, only listened in on the radio."

"He was ace James. He knows he's a racehorse that one, just needs to be left to make the right choices himself. He broke well, chopped through the rough ground no bother and got on with his job. He's as tough as old boots!" Clare was triumphant in her appraisal of Buzz's performance.

"Tough eh… hmmmm …tough enough for snow?" asked James.

"What do you mean?"

"St. Moritz is what I mean. He's proven himself today in awful conditions for his first race out. He's overcome his loading fears, arrived here today and knuckled down," explained James.

"Are you asking me, or are you telling me?" replied Clare slowly, almost nervously.

"Awww, come on Jonesy. Don't be like that! I think he could do it. He's tough. You said so yourself."

"Tough James is one thing. Travelling across Europe and galloping on snow hoping to win, is another," she gasped. "Christ until the week before last we couldn't even load him!"

"I know, and look what you've achieved with him in that time. He's got ability, he's trainable and he's tough."

"Who are you trying to convince James, me or you?" Clare looked across at James. She knew how much he hankered after another chance on the 'White Turf'. What harm could training Buzz for it do? After all, she knew herself he was a capable horse. A smile broke out across her face and that smile said it all. They were going to train him for St. Moritz.

Chapter 6

At Haydock, the decision had been made. Clare and James were preparing Buzz to run in the February 2003, American Express Grosser Preis, in St. Moritz. This was a listed race, which meant that the calibre of horses entered was high and the prize money pot was set accordingly at £23,809. Prize money would be paid out to fifth place. It was on snow, over 1 mile and 2 furlongs. To be eligible, Buzz was required to have won £12,500 prize money from his previous races. His winnings would also dictate the weight the horse carried on the day. On that basis, James scrutinised the racing calendar for suitable races, ensuring his potential total winnings from those races would deem him eligible.

There were other variables which also had to be considered in the finely balanced equation. Buzz would need to learn to make long journeys alone. There would be a ferry crossing and probably an overnight stop to factor in. He would need to be mentally tough enough to get to St. Moritz, accept the ice and snow, then perform on it as he would on the all-weather track; without hesitation or question. James would need to very carefully select the jockey, as it would seem Buzz preferred to win under his own steam, without too much in the way of interference from his pilot. The last, but not least unwelcome variable would be Alistair and Miranda. Would they permit their horse to run abroad? He didn't want the added pressure of them knowing his intentions at that point. After all, just because he wanted to take Buzz to St. Moritz it was still a long way off.

These were just a few of the issues to consider. There were still plenty of logistical problems, mainly associated with the smooth running of the yard in their absence and the consistent training of the remaining horses. Above all, Buzz had to be eligible. One win at Haydock didn't make him a champion and it didn't get him an entry.

James found several suitable races over the mile. Ripon, York and Epsom were the first in late August and into September. Buzz needed to accept the travelling involved in getting to the various race meets without issue. They knew that the horse loved to run, perhaps on his own terms, but he loved his job and he knew in essence that he was born to race. As his reward for good travelling behaviour, he could run. At least that was the plan!

Regarding Alistair and Miranda, they were still revelling in the win at Haydock, so racing their winning horse at courses up and down the country was music to their ears. Miranda spent every opportunity bragging and name dropping horrendously. She invited all and sundry to watch 'her Buzz'. Clare's skin would crawl when Miranda referred to him that way.

"Her Buzz! In her dreams! She might own you on paper, but she doesn't know you at all, and you don't know her! She's a pathetic joke of a woman. To be honest I pity her Buzz, I really do, sad miserable woman!" Clare muttered away to Buzz like a pensioner having a blue rinse at the salon. He listened, as intently as ever whilst slowly and methodically chewing his hay. "You're a tramp, you know that. Your box is filthy. You walk it all in and mix it all up. Why can't you just poo in one corner like Tigress? She's a nice clean girl, unlike you, you old tramp!" He still chomped away, indifferent to her complaints.

James walked into the barn looking for her. He had entered Buzz for the mile at Ripon on the 31st August. He wanted to talk it through with Clare and potentially adjust his work pattern accordingly. He knew exactly where to find her. Looking down the barn he spied Rascal sitting looking directly into the box where no doubt he would find Clare. The dog and the horse were contentedly listening to her belly aching about: Miranda, Buzz's box, the economic state of the country and the latest farrier's bill. It was all the same to them, her voice was good enough, the topic irrelevant.

"I've entered him for Ripon. He seems to come out of these races as fresh as a daisy, ready for the next one." She continued sorting through the bed for muck and chucking it with the kind of well perfected flick that one only achieves after years of stable duties.

"Then there's York and Epsom in September, Richard's free for Ripon, but Dennis Noles will have to do the other two. Think Buzz will run for Dennis?" James knew the jockey's traits. Some would follow trainers' instructions and some were more 'gung ho' and felt that they had the final say. After all, it was the jockeys' out there being followed round by an ambulance, not the trainer.

"Maybe, I'll think on it. It's early days yet." Noncommittal, she scooped up the barrow and made for the muck heap bidding Buzz good night as she went. James and Rascal followed obediently.

Clare had always been involved with horses in one way or another. Having owned her first pony when she was only nine years old, Fircone had been a Christmas present from her parents. The eye catching, Welsh Section B gelding had started a love affair that would last a lifetime for Clare. She kept her own horses and worked in yards throughout her teens. At school she dreamed of horses and after school she rode them. Horses, horses, horses, oh and more horses. That was the top and bottom of Clare Jones. After finishing her secondary education, she moved away from the Midlands where she was born and raised, and went to work in Newmarket. Clare happened to arrived in Newmarket shortly after James' time there came to an end. She rode out for Paul Kelleway before moving to Epsom where she rode flat horses for Terry Mills and Brian McMahon and also tried her hand riding some point to point horses at a local yard.

After that Clare moved away from riding for a career and worked briefly in the financial sector. She loathed it and it wasn't long before she was back in the Midlands looking for riding work. Coincidentally, James Unett, an up and coming trainer, who had recently been granted his trainers licence at Dunstall Park, was looking for Christmas staff. Clare joined the team on a temporary basis, but by the February had started full time. James could see her natural ability with the horses and wanted her on his yard. The rest, as they say is history!

They had a little over three weeks until the run at Ripon. Buzz was kept on the normal exercise regime. He was Clare's ride. She put her all into him, working out feed rations and ingredients specific for him. Using Echinacea to boost his immune system and a deer antler supplement to aid joint repair and regeneration, her plan was to build his strength from the inside out. Although he came out of his races bouncing and seemed able to wear the inevitable strain all athlete's experience, Clare knew he had a tall order to meet and she intended to prepare him fully for it.

She gained valuable riding knowledge from him. He didn't like to be badgered into running. He had a Buzz operated barometer. If he wanted to, he would run like the wind and if he didn't, he wouldn't. It was that simple. He clearly felt he had the right to choose for himself. The very same bloody minded qualities, that were intrinsic for the winning combination in St. Moritz, could easily be his undoing. Consistency wasn't his strong point but Clare was beavering away testing and asking him questions during his work, trying to get to the bottom of him. She found he didn't favour chasing others around the track. He liked to be ahead from the off, making all, leading the pack. When he broke clear and clean from the stalls, he covered so much ground that he could set himself in front of the pack. Clare felt this was the key to keeping him focussed on the winning post. She also noticed that when he had to catch up with others, the leaning and veering across the track started, losing valuable time and wasting energy; although he had the scope to gain ground he wouldn't always have the track space to do it. Making all and getting ahead was vital for Buzz.

This had not been the case at Haydock and James was struggling to agree with Clare. He felt that the horse had the ability to perform wherever he found himself in the pack. Clare didn't dispute he could pull it out of the bag if he needed to, but she wanted to race him in the way Buzz liked it best. A happy horse works well, and she repeated that mantra to James every time they talked tactics about Buzz.

As the Ripon race grew nearer, Clare became increasingly preoccupied with Buzz's run. She wanted him to run well and she wanted James to edge that much closer to his dream of running him at St. Moritz. However, the pressure was hers to bear alone. Buzz remained blissfully unaware, whilst James believed it was a forgone conclusion. Clare felt the weight saddled to her, as race day crept closer and closer. James agreed that she should drive Buzz and lead him up. Usually the Trainer endeavours to be with his horses when they ran, but James knew that Clare was more than capable of managing on her own. Besides, the downside of running a smaller, more personal yard, was that the team was stretched staffing wise and both Clare and James leaving the yard for the day was logistically difficult. He therefore decided to remain at home and send Michelle to saddle up. James had nothing else running at Ripon that day which meant Buzz would have to travel alone. Clare felt this was a step too far for Buzz to deal with at this stage, so the services of 'Tiny', the yard's resident pony, were employed to keep him company in the lorry. Most competitive yards have a companion pony to aid travel, turn out and recuperation periods and Clare and James were no exception. Tiny was a 10 hand, piebald mare. Her exact age was unknown, but judging by her teeth she was put somewhere around five years old, but given her relative youth she was like a wise, old owl. To a horse, size is irrelevant and this was never more evident than with Tiny, who could keep even the biggest and meanest horses in the yard in check!

On 31st August Clare, Michelle, Buzz and Tiny left for Ripon to run Buzz in the Tote Exacta Handicap. Buzz loaded well. Clare could have sworn he looked amused by Tiny's petulant face peeking under the partition, and as usual he christened his departure with a kick, kick, kick!

The drive was uneventful and once they had arrived and settled Buzz and Tiny, Clare hunted down Richard Kelly, Buzz's partner that day. Discovering that he was riding in the current race, she returned to the yard. He was drawn 7 of 8 which was less than ideal. It was a wide draw so he would have more ground to cover. The horses on the inside would easily get ahead and Richard would have to drive him on.

Once saddled, Clare led him to the parade ring where it was quieter than Haydock and considerably drier! The race time was 3.50pm. Alistair and Miranda were mincing about, talking to other owners in the ring, with Miranda mentioning in an overly loud tone that 'her Buzz' had won last time out at Haydock. She looked ridiculous thought Clare. The hat she was wearing made her look like a peacock and her skin tight dress with the slit up to her thigh, revealed enough leg to make a Moulin Rouge dancer blush.

"Trashy and ridiculous," Clare whispered in Buzz's ear. With that he kicked out as though in agreement.

After one circuit she spotted Richard. He was approaching slowly, sizing up Buzz as he jogged on the spot. Although keen, he wasn't bouncing. Clare thought he was too calm, if anything.

"You're drawn wide, so get a clean break and make all if you can. Don't hit him Richard, it doesn't work. Oh, and he might lean a bit, be ready," Clare spoke the words imploringly.

Richard Kelly was a good friend of Shane O'Neil. Shane O'Neil had ridden Buzz at Dunstall Park in July and Buzz had run badly. The racing community was a small world and Shane had called the horse everything from a pig to a dog, to the extent where Richard initially didn't want the ride. It wasn't long though before his competitive nature got the better of him and he decided he would ride Buzz and that he would do a better job of it than Shane.

With Richard legged up, they cantered out onto the track. In normal Buzz style, he gave an excited buck. Harsh in his response, Richard shortened the reins and drove him forward telling Buzz he wouldn't tolerate any of his nonsense! And so the battle began. By the time the stalls opened and the race started, Buzz had shut down. Although he broke clean and fast and surprisingly led, he remained at that pace. He neither weakened nor did he lengthen for home. Clare sunk onto the rails as 7 horses breezed past him on the home straight. Richard was flapping like a chicken and by the time Clare got to him he was red in the face and indignant. Buzz on the other hand had barely broken a sweat.

"Shane's right, it's a bloody pig!" He leapt down from Buzz's back and snatched at the girth straps pulling at them to release the saddle, so he could go and weigh in. Clare remained silent. Not a believer in 'I told you so', she started the cool down, rugging him as she walked away. Unlike everyone else in the equation, the jockey still got paid for the ride regardless of the end result. Clare always thought it ought to operate on a no win, no fee basis! After all, those were the terms of her employment!

"I saw that buck. You're a bugger! Bet he thought he'd fall off, jabbed you in the gob did he? Held on for dear life by the look of your mouth mate! Calls himself a jockey, he's a bloody amateur," Clare vented as she walked but Buzz looked unfazed. Used to that kind of rough handling, he dealt with it accordingly and didn't win.

The phone went off in her pocket and at the same time Alistair appeared. James would have to wait she thought.

"What happened there then Clare?" asked Alistair as he sauntered over. He had a look of strain and acceptance. A beaten look! His suit

was well fitted, and although jaded, Clare could see that once upon a time he would have been an attractive man. Although life had treated him well financially, he was a sad man. Sad and unhappy with his lot, thought Clare.

"He broke well, and led the pack Alistair. I think he just faded, that's all. He isn't going to win every race he runs and he did try." Clare responded defensively, she immediately regretted it.

"I don't feel that tone is altogether necessary! I only asked what happened! Miranda's bleating in the bar and I just wanted something to tell her."

"I'm going to return James' call now and get Buzz back to the yard. Enjoy your evening and say hi to Miranda." It was the best she could manage.

Dialling James, it rang just the once.

"Well?"

"It was Richard. He wouldn't have it James. I told you Buzz won't be treated like that. He doesn't run that way," she blurted.

"He has to run either way Clare. He's a bloody racehorse, not a pop star!" James was exasperated. "He led and then stayed. Showed us what he can do and then sat there like a goose's arse while the rest of the field went home! He's taking the piss is what he's doing!"

The next thing Clare heard was the click of the receiver going down, followed by the dialling tone.

****

Dennis Noles rode Buzz on 4th September at York, in the Irwins Stake Apprentice Handicap. An 'apprentice race' is a race for jockeys who are not yet classed as professional. To be classed as a 'professional', a jockey must have ridden in 100 races. This is referred to as 'riding out your claim'. Apprentices are paid half the professional jockey fee plus expenses, and only if the trainer is so minded. Drawn 8 meant a mid-field start and they switched sharply to the left of the track soon after the start and settled in behind the leaders. Dennis drove him home, finishing fourth out of 22 runners, beaten by Silvertown, Ruby Legend and Rolway Ritz.

All Clare kept repeating was that there was too much interference from the jockeys. They HAD to trust him, go with him and not dictate to him. He had still won £630 for his placing, but that barely covered the cost of entry and travel.

****

On 11th September at 3.55pm, Dennis rode him again. This time over the mile at Epsom in the MAN Apprentice Stakes. Drawn 8 of 8, once again he had a wide draw. He wasn't ever in the running. Driven straight for home, Dennis used his stick but to no avail. Buzz finished second to last.

As Pay the Silver, the winner, waltzed into the winner's enclosure right under Miranda's nose, she was already complaining that Buzz was a loser. It was everyone else's fault. She blamed the horse, the jockey, the trainer, Clare and even the weather. Prattling on to Alistair continuously, like a whinging child about wanting to win and not just follow Buzz about like a groupie, Alistair felt like he needed to act. He had to be seen by Miranda to be doing something. Nearly last was more than his little angel could stomach and so he called James.

"We need to improve this horse's performance James. He needs to earn his keep! I am paying you well enough so why isn't the horse even in the running?"

"Alistair, he's a horse not a machine and sometimes a horse like Buzz needs to find himself. He'll come right. He knows his job and will produce the goods but just needs to figure it out."

"Figure it out? What are you talking about? He needs to bloody win James, and you need to train him with that in mind." Alistair didn't mince his words.

After the run at Epsom, Clare decided Buzz should try running in blinkers and head gear. She knew that he liked to get his head out in front and be the lead and blinkers would stop him from being able to see the horses that were behind and to the side of him. She wanted him to feel in control and hoped it would be a technique that would improve his form. It worked to a degree in training but as they only exercised in twos and threes, he was never really put fully to the test.

September 25th Buzz ran at Chester in the Saffie Joseph & Sons Handicap, drawn 9 out of 16. Wide again! It was a big field and Tom Fann was his jockey. Finishing seventh, he ran a better race technically. He chased the leaders and was ridden out well over the last 3 furlongs.

He made ground in the final furlong but simply not enough to gain a place. However the winner was only 1 length in front of him overall.

Clare was pleased, he had tried, had made ground up and had wanted to run. James too noted the difference and even Alistair commented that the horse had looked like he'd tried today. The pressure wasn't off though. If Buzz didn't start winning some prize money, Alistair and Miranda would be sure to pull the plug. No training fees meant, no training. Worse still, they could pull him out from Clare and James' yard and give him to another trainer to produce the results which they were so hungry for. St. Moritz had not even been mentioned yet. It had gone back to being an unspoken white elephant between Clare and James.

Impressed by his riding, James decided to ask Tom Fann to ride him again on his next run in the Blanchisseuse Handicap. Thankfully Alistair and Miranda couldn't attend. It was a rarity but James was grateful for small mercies! However his luck stopped there. Drawn wide again, Buzz missed the start. He chased down the leaders, striding out confidently in his headgear but it was never going to be enough. After giving it his all to catch them up, he didn't have enough in the tank to finish the job and ended up eleventh out of 17 runners. James was flat, Clare deflated and Buzz indifferent. The only person who was thrilled was Tom Fann. Elated, he crowed to James about the power he felt when Buzz was trying to catch the leaders. For the first time, one of Buzz's jockeys had truly seen what Clare had seen; the strength and ability that pumped through Buzz when he really wanted it and when he really dug in was awesome. Perhaps the tables had turned!

****

Perked up by the run at Pontefract, James artfully waylaid Alistair's fears on the lack of performance and dangled a carrot by way of a long weekend of racing, this time in Ayr, Scotland. Buzz was entered to run on two consecutive days, the 14th and 15th of October. This would be a test of Buzz's resilience. He had been coping with the travelling aspect well and both Clare and James were happy that although he kicked and banged about en route, Buzz was exhibiting his excitement and anticipation of the race he was travelling to, rather than displaying fear or anxiety about the travelling itself. Good old Tiny had also been clocking up the mileage, keeping company with Buzz in the lorry and becoming quite a seasoned traveller herself!

Few racehorses would physically be able to run two races back to back only a day apart and James was excited by the prospect. Coupling the trip with a short shooting break, (James' favoured past time when away from the yard) he was counting down the days to the trip. The yard would be managed by Michelle (and Rascal) in their absence. Clare would drive the lorry to Scotland on the eve of the race and meet James at the course. Alistair and Miranda had arranged a flight and for James to meet them at the airport and them to on the hotel for dinner and drinks. Well at least, that was the plan!

After a long day's pheasant shooting and probably a few too many toddies with the keeper on the shoot, James headed for Ayr racecourse. Clare had arrived and was settling Buzz into his stable when James' Landrover rattled through the Scottish rain into the car park. Horrified, she checked her watch. What was he doing here? Alistair and Miranda's plane would have landed by now and he was supposed to be there to collect them! Pushing James into the passenger seat, she proceeded to bawl him out for being so stupid and took off at high speed for the airport. James thought it was extremely funny and sat fumbling in the dark trying to roll a fag, pieces of tobacco flicking everywhere whilst Clare concentrated in the dark searching desperately for signs to the airport.

"I am so sorry Miranda," Clare spluttered as she fell out of the Landrover, banging her shin on the kickboard. "Ouch! James! Wake up. Get out and help Alistair with his bags!" She glared at James as he sleepily roused himself from the car.

"I'm coming, I'm coming!" he muttered under his breath. "Miranda darling you look marvellous!"

Miranda looked furious, not marvellous. They had been waiting for nearly an hour and a half for James to collect them and then to add insult to injury he had arrived, clearly having had a skin full and in a filthy Landrover.

"Where on earth have you been?" she exploded.

"Never mind, come on get in the car Miranda." Alistair ushered her towards the car.

"I'm not getting in that! You must be joking! Alistair, order a cab.

My Louis Vuitton isn't going anywhere near that filthy rust bucket. How dare you leave us standing here waiting! You disgust me, the pair of you! Look at yourself Clare. You're covered in muck and your hair's a state! Have you no shame? And James, you're nothing but a drunken fool! No wonder your horses never win anything. You couldn't win an egg and spoon race!" She was vicious! In a full display of her true colours, she verbally cut Clare like a knife. "Running around after him, just like you do with those horses. Pathetic! Totally pathetic!"

Before Clare had a chance to respond, James had marched round to the front of the car and stepped up to Miranda. Instantly sobering up after hearing her outburst at Clare, James verbally launched at Miranda.

"I'll tell you what's pathetic Miranda. You! Your fame hungry, sad little life makes me sick. You turn up at race meets dressed like a tart, you drink until he's so embarrassed by your behaviour that he takes you home. You're a laughing stock! Did you know that? If you ever talk to Clare that way again, there will be hell to pay! She's twice the lady you'll ever be!"

Silence fell. Slapped down like the child she was, Miranda had no response. Alistair stunned, stood in the dripping rain unsure of what his next move should be.

"Enough of all that. Everyone's tired so get in and we'll take you back to the hotel." Ever conciliatory, Clare reached forward and picked up the bags. What she was really thinking was that she needed to get to Buzz. All this nonsense was taking up her time.

The ride back to the hotel was quiet to say the least. Clare dropped them in the foyer and headed back to Buzz. She needed to feed him his dinner and dress him over for the night. James made his way to the hotel bar, where, after a short time, he was surprised to be joined by Alistair. He held his hand out to James.

"Well done old boy," Alistair said. "I've never heard anyone speak to her in that way and it's just what the doctor ordered! Let's have a drink!"

There were 20 runners in the Lochranza Handicap and Buzz was drawn 4. For once, a decent enough draw and Tom Fann was happy enough with that. As Buzz trotted to the stalls, Tom was quietly hoping he'd have another thrilling ride today. Smiling as he remembered

Buzz's sheer force, he patted his neck and spoke kindly to the horse. Loading took a while as one of the horses was playing up, refusing to go in. The stalls handler blindfolded it eventually and gave it the heave ho. In it went.

"Hoods off!" The command came and a split second later they were off.

Buzz broke and hung right. He raced wide and prominent and found himself in the lead pack. 3 furlongs out, he dug in and ran for home. Unexpectedly though, the two horses to his left struck heels. The first stumbled causing Buzz to break his momentum. He broke his stride, and changed his leading leg ready to push on but it was too late. The front runners, who had been completely unaffected by this were well ahead and he finished sixth.

The unfolding drama had been witnessed by all spectators, including Alistair and Miranda. After the previous evening's debacle, Miranda was on her best behaviour and even she could see that it was a pure accident that Buzz didn't get placed.

"Never mind! There's always tomorrow," she said refreshingly.

As expected, Buzz came out of the first race well. All attention was now focussed on the next race, tomorrow afternoon. After an enjoyable evening's entertainment at the hotel, Clare retired early, savouring the lavish room and lack of mucking out duties. She soaked in the bath for an hour before curling up in bed, where she slept soundly until the following morning. Fresh and keen, she jumped out of bed and headed straight for the yard.

"Morning lad," she said as she slipped into Buzz's box. Tiny nickered from the box next door. "Yes, good morning to you too Tiny tots!" Clare called back. Checking his rugs were OK, she ran her hand down his shoulder. He was snuggly warm. He nudged her with his head. She knew that nudge well. It translated to, "Breakfast please?" Off she trotted to prepare the morning feed and to start mucking out. Buzz's race wasn't until 2.20pm; it was going to be a long morning. Would it be worth the wait?

There were 18 runners in the Port Patrick Selling Stakes. Lady luck wasn't especially on their side and again he had an average draw of 9! Poor Buzz, he always had to make up ground. Draws were pulled from a hat. It was quite literally, 'the luck of the draw'. Both Tom and Buzz knew what they had to do. Tom intended to break and make all, no

messing; he was counting on Buzz's ability to carry them round and that is exactly what happened. Buzz broke, held straight and motored on making impressive headway. The two horses with the inside draw were naturally leading, but not by much and Buzz kicked on home. Today there were no dramas and no distractions. Buzz got his head down and galloped past the winning post in second place, just behind Erupt. James was thrilled! To have run back to back, improved over those two days and run a wide race, due to his draw, was a real testament to Buzz's attitude and ability. More importantly for James, Buzz was ticking all the boxes for St. Moritz. He was also £902 pounds closer to the £12,500 target.

Alistair and Miranda celebrated in their usual style. The incident at the airport long forgotten, by them at least, it was champagne all round. She swanned around the winners' enclosure like a model on the cat walk, but to Clare, she paled into insignificance compared to her Buzz. Second was more than good enough for her. He had tried his best run an honest race and given it his all, despite his previous run 24 hours earlier. He was a serious horse and to Clare he was hers!

Chapter 7

November brought the rain, a stressful week of managing frightened horses, (due to firework displays) two runs away and Buzz, Tigress and Polar Dance at home. Over the mile, for Fight the Feeling and Urban Myth at Southwell on the 9th, Buzz on the 13th, Tigress the 15th and Polar Dance on the 21st at Dunstall Park. After the back to back runs at Ayr, Clare and James had given Buzz a month away from running. Besides that, there were other horses that needed their attention and never ending owners to please.

Due to strict racing regulations on sedating racehorses, Clare was unable to medically help her horses through the stressful time that was Guy Fawkes and Bonfire Night. She was exhausted. Whilst the Great British public burned their guys and lit their rockets, horses across the land quaked in their boxes. Some closed their eyes and shook until it was over, whilst some reared and spun, sweating in fear. Whether their fear was external or internal, Clare had to soothe, calm and relax the horses in her care. With each bang and peppering of light across the sky, the horses flinched and shuddered. In some cases, so tense they were unable to eat or drink. Clare virtually slept in the barn. Most displays end around 11pm, so by the time she settled the horses down and made sure they weren't sweating up or colicking, it was usually getting on for 12pm. Stable duties started again at 5.30am. Five and a half hours sleep, night after night, just wasn't enough when the job was so physically demanding. James offered to take over but he knew it was fruitless. Even if she'd accepted, Clare would never have slept soundly. She would only have dozed half asleep, listening out for her horses.

Buzz coped reasonably well but Tigress, a petite dark bay filly, with the prettiest of heads, hated it. She sweated buckets and dropped weight and condition terribly during that time. Buckets of water filled with electrolytes were in every corner of her box trying to tempt her to drink her fill and replenish her fluid loss.

Just as quickly as they came, they went again and normal service was resumed. First up, were the runs at Southwell for Fight the Feeling and Urban Myth. Packing them off to Southwell, Clare waved James and Michelle off in the lorry. This time, she stayed behind at the yard doing morning stables with Rascal. Quietly relieved, she finished up and headed for a well-deserved snuggle on the sofa.

Urban Myth was James' first winner as a licenced trainer. James had a soft spot for him and although in James' mind he owed him nothing, the horse loved a run. You would know when he needed one because he would be so fit and so ready, he'd go off his food. James would enter him and run him, then Myth would come home and eat up. James was hopeful for him that day. Fight the Feeling was going out for the placing. It was a stiff race for him with some well rated horses but James' motto was that you had to be in it to win it! Southwell is an all-weather track but the surface was known for being very deep. This made the kick back awful, regardless of the weather. Horses worked hard at Southwell.

The next thing Clare knew, she was woken by the phone. It was James.

"Put Channel 4 on Jonesy!" was all she heard. Flicking on the TV, she instantly recognised the big white blaze that was George's face and behind him the huge 1st sign! He'd won! She could see James and his owners shaking hands and popping a bottle of champagne. Wowee she thought.

That was a significant win for George. He had run against horses rated nearly 10 above him. Suddenly, James appeared on the screen.

"Congratulations Mr Unett. What did you think of Fight the Feeling's run?" asked the Channel 4 pundit.

"We knew he had it in him and he proved us right! It was well worth the drive!" replied James.

Cheeky sod thought Clare. He could bluff his way out of Alcatraz that Unett!

Urban Myth was running in the second to last race. Channel 4 racing wouldn't be covering it, so Clare would have to listen to the race commentary on the radio. Checking her watch as she wandered through to the kitchen, she flicked on the kettle and tuned in the ancient, paint splattered radio. The race was just about to start. The commentator soon announced that they were all loaded and ready to run.

"And they're off! And boy, are they off! The pace here is fast! Priceless is leading the field, followed by Ladies Man in the green sleeves. Behind them in the red hat is Cash Code. But wait,... Urban Myth's been pulled up! He's out of the running...!"

After that, the commentary became a blur for Clare! She couldn't hear the words coming from the speaker as she frantically stabbed James' number into the phone. No answer! She knew he'd be in a track car, driving with the course vet to where Urban Myth had been pulled up. Those next few minutes were agonisingly long, until finally the phone rang. Grabbing the receiver, she answered.

"James? What's happened? Is he ok?"

"He's gone Clare! His tendon snapped! Vet said it was too far gone. Not worth scanning." When James spoke the words he was devoid of any emotion. Racing involved risk. Everyone in the industry knew that, but one should not underestimate the pain that trainers feel, when a horse breaks down during a race. James knew why Urban Myth's tendon had snapped. That little horse had tried too hard! He'd loved to gallop so very much that he'd over reached with his hind leg and struck his foreleg, slicing through the soft tissue and the tendon. That little horse had some heart.

Distraught, Clare ran to the barn. She went hurtling past the empty boxes, barely able to look and straight to box 25, Buzz's box. Wrapping her arms around his neck, she sobbed into his mane. Buzz stood still, sensing that it was his turn to give a soothing talk for a change. Clare didn't cope well with the loss of a horse. A strapping two year old colt playing up on the gallop was no match for this tough little red head but she, Clare, was nothing more than a fragile child when faced with the death of a horse.

The next few days at Dunstall Park were quiet ones. James expressed emotion in a strikingly similar way to Buzz. Everyone knew about it. He shouted orders, barking at the staff, Clare included, about the most minor of things. Deeply saddened by the loss of Urban Myth,

he buried himself in work, avoiding the thinking time he couldn't yet face. The empty box on the yard, a sharp reminder that on the 9th two horses had left to run but only one returned home.

The morning of the 13th arrived. Buzz was primped and plaited by Clare in readiness for the day's racing. Tack polished, silks pressed and bagged, they were ready. By lunchtime, the usual race day fever pitch at Dunstall Park was building. The horseboxes were pulling in and the car park starting to fill. The horses fed off the vibe and were excited and alert. Their heads peering out from their stables, watching and listening, some even calling to the visiting horses arriving in dribs and drabs from all over the country.

Buzz had an early run, 2.25pm, in the Crowns Kitchen and Bedrooms at Waterline Handicap. Clare was pleased as this meant: she could lead him up, watch the race and get him back to the barn and settled, in a reasonable time frame. Buzz's routine wouldn't be too up skittled. He would be back in his box for tea time, along with the rest of the barn.

Buzz was bouncing as she led him across the car park. He danced sideways, kick, kick, kick went the right hind. In the paddock he was fresh. Jog, jog, kick, jog, jog, he went. He looked fabulous! Every inch the racer! However, today Clare didn't have time to admire the horse. She was struggling to hold onto him! Suddenly, he reared up, standing tall on his hind legs and striking out with his forelegs. Clare loosened the rope to give him some room but she wasn't fast enough. As he came down, legs flailing, he struck her across the chest. Crashing backwards, Clare fell, badly winded by the blow. The crowd of onlookers gasped in shock and fell silent while James grabbed Buzz's rein. Still dancing and prancing, unaware of what he'd done, Buzz snorted and rolled his eyes at James. The paddock steward helped Clare to her feet and attempted to usher her from the ring. She was having none of it!

"I'm fine, thank you. Really I'm fine," she squeaked as she stood up shakily. "I have to lead him up."

"Jonesy go back home. I'll do it," ordered James, but it was futile. Clare had no intention of going home. She wouldn't have been anywhere else, other than right there with Buzz.

"No! He's going to win today!"

Shane O'Neil sauntered over and Clare looked puzzled. She thought

Tom was riding Buzz today. James looked suitably sheepish! He hadn't wanted her to know until the last minute that there had been a jockey change and that the only available jockey was Shane.

"Oh bloody hell! This just gets better and better! Right, listen here Shane. I know you don't like him but this horse will win today if you just sit tight. Get him out in front and he'll do the rest. Are you listening? No whip, just a light hand! Got it?"

Wise enough to know not to answer her back, Shane glanced over at James, who nodded and raised his eyebrows in agreement. Clare got back on the business end, while James legged Shane up. And with that, they led him out to the track.

Clare's chest was burning but she stood by the track entrance, gripping the rails as she watched Buzz and Shane canter round to the stalls. He loaded easily, drawn 9 of 12, she would have to try and pick out his red head gear if she were to have any hope of seeing him break. They were off! She couldn't make him out but then there he was, just behind the leaders. Wringing her hands together, Clare could barely watch as this normally spelled disaster. Not today. Buzz got into his stride, slowly but surely and he was gaining. Praying that Shane would give him his head, Clare stared into the distance as the horses rounded the final bend. The commentator was shouting:

"Bressbee is making a run for it. Answered Promise and On Guard are the front runners, but here he comes. Make no mistake, he's travelling with Shane O'Neil putting in minimal effort. Answered Promise is weakening now and is back to third. Now its Bressbee and On Guard fighting for first place! They're in the final furlong now and Bressbee's inching past him, now, ooooo! That's a photo finish for Bressbee and On Guard!"

Buzz and the remaining runners thundered right past Clare, where she was stood waiting by the track entrance. Shane O'Neil was grinning from ear to ear.

"There you go James. I knew he'd do it today. I could feel it."

"Hang on, we don't know yet. They haven't called it," said James. But they both knew that either way, Buzz had run an extremely professional race.

Shane was trotting back over when the results were announced.

"Bressbee first, On Guard in second and Answered Promise in third."

As they made their way to the winners' enclosure, Clare caught a glimpse of Miranda. Today's colour of choice was burgundy. For once she had toned the outfit down and was in a well cut trouser suit. Sadly though, the shrieking and hooting remained unchanged and Clare could hear the usual nonsense being spouted about 'her Buzz'. When they entered the enclosure, Alistair could be seen shaking hands with the race sponsor's representative. Probably ordering a new kitchen, thought Clare as she was summoned over with Buzz for a posed photo. Clare hated the 'grip and grin' shots from the races preferring the motion shots, where the horse's energy and movement were captured in the frame.

Shane hopped off to weigh in. Passing Clare he whispered, "Good call Jonesy. He's learned his job hasn't he?"

Clare smiled adoringly at Buzz.

"No," she said. "He knew it all along."

"Well done Buzz. You are a clever horsey," cooed Miranda. "Take him back Clare and come for a drink." Groaning internally, Clare couldn't think of anything worse!

"Sorry Miranda. I'm on evening stable duties but James will join you shortly. Besides, my chest is hurting a bit after that." She smiled at James triumphantly. That'll teach him for not telling me Shane had the ride. She smiled to herself smugly, as she led him around the cool down paddock. She had known he would win today. She'd felt it! Buzz had just earned a further £2,954 in prize money, making the total £8,518 so far. He wasn't far short now of the £12,500 he needed for the Grosser Preis.

More importantly for Clare, this time, they had put a smile on James' face. Since the tragedy of Urban Myth, James had been sullen and withdrawn and quite awful to live with. It was understandable but knowing James as she did, this win would be just the tonic he needed to revive him again. She made a mental note to rub some arnica into her chest. Bloody Buzz she chuckled.

****

Edging closer and closer to their target became a source of anxiety for James. The, 'would they? wouldn't they?' mind games had started. James so wanted his chance. He desperately wanted to run a horse at

St. Moritz under his own name. He just didn't want to quite let himself believe it could be happening. When Buzz came fourth in the Littlewoods Bet Direct Handicap, on the 7th December at Dunstall Park, it didn't do much to bolster him up. Despite the previous run and the lessons learned by the jockey, on this run, Shane said that he felt Buzz needed some more encouragement and used his stick. Consequently, they lost pace 3 furlongs out and although stayed in the final furlong, finished fourth.

"Not exactly superstar material," spat James to Clare, over dinner that evening.

Silence was her response.

"He's got one more crack at it on Boxing Day, then that's it, game over."

More silence followed by the scraping of the chair on the linoleum floor, as she cleared her plate from the table and left the room. The pressure between them had been building, brewing behind the scenes for weeks. Clare felt a mixture of understanding and sympathy towards James. She knew how important the St. Moritz race was to him on a personal level. She could identify with James' burning ambition to achieve his goal. In essence a trainer's base persona had to include a strong competitive streak and that would inevitably spill over into everyday life, but she almost wanted to switch it off. She was so in love with Buzz and so proud of his achievements, that although running him at St. Moritz seemed possible, it wasn't a burning desire for her. Stifled by ignorant jockeys and the multitude of opinion surrounding the horse himself, she felt like his only defender. Her love for him was unconditional, whether he ran badly and lost or ran well and won. To her he had come so far in such a short space of time. He'd grown from a burned out, mean tempered beast, to the glistening horse he now was, with both his form and record greatly improved. James was so focussed on the bigger prize, it was almost like he couldn't see the wood for the trees. He kept pushing and pushing. Pushing her and Buzz to their limit.

It was a quiet Christmas that year. James' family were scattered across the country, so visiting became virtually impossible with all the horses to manage and Clare's parents were away themselves for the holiday period. Clare had zoned into her work. In contrast to James, she withdrew when under pressure. Quietly busy, she threw herself

into her duties. She usually had five horses under her care but over the holiday period that had increased to eight, as Michelle's horses, Billboa, Polar Dance and Bronte's Star were included into her rota over the holiday period.

Billboa had been off after a wind operation and was being brought back into work slowly. He had started cantering again and Clare was enjoying the ride. He was a keen horse, perhaps a little too keen and his exuberance reminded her of Urban Myth. Billboa hadn't quite mastered the art of racing, enjoying the game of the gallops but never really applying himself. He had ability but his concentration was poor. Too easily distracted, he would spook at everything, even things he had seen time and time again, like a wheelbarrow on the yard! Clare enjoyed the ride because he kept his rider thinking and he certainly reminded jockeys of the importance of a good seat.

Then there was Polar Dance, a beautiful 16.2hh dapple grey gelding with a black mane and tail, who had quite a following at Dunstall Park. He was the fastest horse they had in training and he knew it. His party trick was to remain in the stalls when they opened at the beginning of a race, refusing to come out. Then, as the other runners took off up the track, suddenly he would leap out and chase them for all he was worth. He hadn't been beaten to date and the crowds loved him. He also had the funny habit of sticking his tongue out at people. Polar Dance was quite a character.

Bronte's Star, a dark bay filly was fairly small at 15.2hh but she was lean and strong. She had a white blaze and four white feet. She had been placed consistently in her races but hadn't really shone and Clare wondered if in fact she would be more suited to another career. Quite often when racehorses don't perform well enough, they are retired from racing and rehomed or sold into other equine disciplines. Some go for show jumping, some for eventing and some for dressage. Clare was very thorough researching the homes she found for her horses, always ensuring they would be well cared for by experienced hands. She hated the term 'failed racer', feeling that they hadn't 'failed' as such but rather, would just be better suited to a different discipline. Clare had seen many ex-racers go on to achieve astounding results and in turn for their second chance, were able to provide some of the best bloodstock genes to those disciplines too, improving the quality and performance within those fields.

After riding Michelle's three daily, she started on her own regulars and first out was always Buzz. She had been working on his pace, keeping him steady and rhythmical, not allowing him to have his head on every piece of exercise and it seemed to be working well. There was a fine balance to be had with him. Ask too much and he went flat but ask too little and he would run erratically, wide and wild across the track. She would mix up her routine with him, keeping him alert and as James had advised, again she worked him clockwise around the track. He wanted him conditioned to run with the rails on his right, as they had done in the beginning to stop him from running wide. This was because although the majority of tracks in the UK were left handed tracks. St. Moritz however was right handed, so the bend was on the other side and so too were the rails.

Clare would work him right handed twice weekly and left handed three times. She found him stiffer to the right, which made sense because his muscles were used to bending left. When a horse canters or gallops, it does so with one foreleg leading the stride. This is called the leading leg. As individuals, horses tend to favour a particular leg, just as people prefer using a right or left hand, and Buzz favoured the left, which suited the left handed tracks more so than the right. Determined to improve him on the right leg, Clare started to take Buzz into the grass field in the centre of the track and work on his movement to condition him to galloping consistently on the correct leg. If Buzz repeatedly changed leg during the race, especially on a corner, he would lose valuable time and potentially his place. Clare knew that in a race this could be the difference between winning and losing. The key to success was through pace and rhythm from the horse and transition work could only help to strengthen and improve his right lead. It wasn't long before Buzz found it easier to bend right and lead correctly with his right. The more he ran that way, the stronger those muscles would be for his race.

****

Boxing Day began with Rascal throwing up all over the sofa. Having stuffed her face with leftover turkey, she had lain bloated on the sofa overnight. But at some point it had clearly got the better of her and Rascal had decided it was better out than in! Repulsed by the smell, Clare stripped off the throw and threw it and the dog outside. The washing she would deal with later!

Buzz was running at 4.15pm in the Littlewoods Bet Direct All Weather Jockey's Championship. In this race, the jockeys were competing for the 'All Weather Championship' and the horses as always for the prize money. This worried Clare tremendously. She couldn't believe that the selected jockey, Dean Wellings, would sit quietly and assist Buzz rather than drive him. She knew if he tried to override the horse, he would remain static and give nothing of himself in the race. She had seen it so many times with Buzz and she was frustrated that all her hard work could so easily be undone by another rider's hands. James had assured her that Dean had been carefully selected and would be sure to take on board the instructions. Clare wasn't so sure.

Once again the routine of grooming and plaiting Buzz for his run began and before she knew where she was, he was plunging around the parade ring on the end of his rope in typical Buzz style. His body hair had been clipped out for the winter season, but his leg hair left on for warmth. He was almost two tone in appearance, his exercise sheet a pale green fleece edged with dark green piping and James' initials, JWU prominently displayed on the side.

Whilst Clare held onto the firework at the end of the rope, James legged Dean Wellings up onto Buzz's back.

"Clare, I'm Dean." Clare looked up at the young lad sitting on top of Buzz. "James tells me you're the person to ask about my instructions for today."

"Erhh, ummm, yes. Right. Well, you see he doesn't like being overdone. He knows his job and judging by the state of him today, he'll win for you but don't hold him too tight. Just a light bit of steering if needed and NO whip! You need to break out, make all and make sure his head's in front, OK? You're drawn 1, so no excuses. He'll do it." Stunned by the initial question, Clare blurted the instructions to the smiling jockey.

"Yes boss. Got that. I'll follow it to the letter, promise!"

When Dean Wellings made a promise, he stuck to it. So when the stalls opened and Buzz jumped out, sticking fast to the rail, Dean took a deep breath and let him go. He wanted the championship so badly, after missing it for the last two years. Now it was his turn. He ran regularly on the all-weather at Dunstall Park and Southwell and he wanted that silverware for himself. He had seen Buzz run and heard the banter in the changing room about Buzz being a double edged sword, powerful beyond belief but quirky with it. None of the previous jockeys had really got his measure and Dean decided that today he would listen to Clare and run it as advised. Buzz made all, leading the field for the entire race. He wasn't challenged once. Flying home past the screaming crowd, he was a horse alone, set apart from the pack, the winner!

Clare and James were thrilled and turned and grabbed each other in a hug.

"Thank you for telling Dean to come to me for instructions. It means a lot," she said in a rare show of affection.

"My pleasure Jonesy," he said squeezing her. "I couldn't face the whinging if I hadn't! We are going Jonesy! That's it! He's done it! That's £5,590 for today, which gets him in!"

An elated Dean and a puffing Buzz appeared back round the track.

"Bloody hell Clare, he can run can't he? Christ that was a breeze. He was on the bridle the whole way round! I haven't ridden one that like for a while!" Dean squeezed the words out through puffs of breath.

"Thanks for trusting him. He's ace! That's just Buzz and just how he runs. Anyhow, there's a silver plate with your name on it I believe!"

Walking past the Owners and Trainers stand, the four made their way to the winner's enclosure. James spotted Simon Owens, a bloodstock agent he'd used once or twice before. Simon was wrapped in a huge coat, hat and scarf and was standing on the balcony talking into his mobile phone. He lifted his glass to James and nodded. Thinking no more of it, James went through the motions in the winner's enclosure. He stood for pictures and made small talk with Alistair and Miranda. Miranda was feeling the cold. No surprise as she was completely under dressed for the December meet. Wearing a short skirt and heels, she was nagging to get back to the bar. Feeling a tap on the shoulder, James turned to find Simon standing behind him.

"Hello mate, long time no see. How've you been?"

"I'm well thanks, you?" James replied shaking Simon's hand.

"I'm all the better for finding this little gem." He placed his hand on Buzz's neck and patted him.

"What do you mean by that Simon?" James said frowning and puzzled.

"You know what I mean. That was a cracking run James. It's about time you let this one go isn't it? Then Simon dropped the bombshell! I have a punter in Surrey wants him for £20,000."

Clare stood reeling in disbelief. Sell him. No way! Surely not! Her mouth felt dry as the panic rose in her stomach. With her eyes she implored James to decline the offer politely but firmly. She knew though that under training rules, the offer would have to be made to the owner.

"Well that's a handsome offer for a horse that's only won a couple of medium rated races," mumbled James. "Put it in writing and we'll talk." James tried to turn away but Simon caught his arm.

"I don't need to put it in writing though, do I James? The owners are up in the bar aren't they?" and with that he turned on his heels and strode off to find Alistair and Miranda.

Clare felt like she'd been punched. She couldn't speak. Horrified that she could lose her Buzz, she fled with him back to the sanctuary of the barn, to hide him from the prying eyes of the agent. What could she do? How could she stop them? She knew that the money hungry Miranda would equate Buzz's sale price with a whole new wardrobe and Alistair would pander to her. She also knew the agent wouldn't let it go. The fee on a £20,000 sale would be huge and business was business. Distraught, she sobbed as she untacked her beautiful boy, stroking and whispering to him as she rugged him. She could taste the salty tears as they flowed. Her Buzz and he was her Buzz in her heart, but the cruel truth was that she didn't own him. In fact, he belonged to Alistair and Miranda and they would do with him what they chose.

Chapter 8

Reflecting the gloomy December weather, James gathered his thoughts. Taking a long hard drag on his cigarette he deliberated his options. His hand had been forced and he had to take action. Standing at the foot of the steps that led up to the Owners and Trainers Lounge, he knew Alistair and Miranda were being groomed by Simon Owens. The first step he decided would be to gauge Alistair and Miranda's reaction to the offer placed on Buzz's head. By now Simon would have buttered them up nicely, promising them the £20,000 for Buzz. No doubt he'd also tell them that he had another promising horse which would suit them better and for a fraction of the cost, neatly doubling his fee! That was the game, he told himself. Horses were trained, improved, then bought and sold for profit. It was business, plain and simple. Battling the rising feeling of resentment, he tried to calm himself. It was infuriating though. All the hard work he had put into Buzz, all the blood, sweat and tears Clare had given to get him into the winners' enclosure, could all be for nothing. In the blink of an eye, his dreams of running Buzz at St. Moritz were looking like nothing more than pie in the sky. He had to try and stop it. He had to somehow say and do something, to keep Buzz with them at Dunstall Park.

Taking a deep breath James marched up the steps into the Owners and Trainers lounge. He fleetingly smiled and acknowledged Den, the security guard, as he congratulated him on his win whilst holding the heavy glass door open for him. Scanning the L shaped room he spotted the threesome standing over to the left of the bar. Perched on a high bar stool, Simon was dripping all over Miranda; his smarmy, calculating style was working a treat on her. Alistair meantime was standing off to the right, looking through the huge windows towards the track. He appeared not to have noticed his wife's advances towards Simon.

Probably doing the maths on the deal, thought James. Ordering a bottle of champagne from the bar, James was going to play this hard. It was either that, or face losing the horse and all chances of St. Moritz.

"What a win!" James raised his hands in victory as he approached Alistair, Miranda and Simon. Holding the champagne in one hand and just three glasses in the other he hugged Miranda, kissing her cheek. "I have to say you look fantastic tonight. You have a very festive glow about you Miranda," he whispered in her ear. Lapping up her compliment and true to form, her attention immediately shifted from Simon to James. 1-0, thought James.

"Have you heard James?" Chirped Miranda. "Simon has a buyer for Buzz! £20,000!"

Shaking Alistair's hand and popping the cork James replied, "Yes. Simon did mention something like that but let's not get carried away. It's Boxing Day and he just won you a fabulous race so let's have a drink and celebrate! Besides, Simon can only buy what is offered for sale!" Turning away from Simon, James poured out three glasses.

"I know James, but Simon here says he has a three year old filly for us to see. A bay. She's in Ireland at the minute and Simon has suggested we go over for the weekend, all expenses paid and see her in training. Simon, would you like a glass?" asked Alistair.

"Simon's not staying, are you Simon?" challenged James staring pointedly at Simon. His eyes said it all. 2-0.

"Apparently not! Here's my card Alistair. Call me. I'll be back in the office on the 28th so we can talk then." Taking his leave, he shook Alistair's hand, politely kissed Miranda goodbye and squeezed her waist just a little too tightly for Alistair's liking. There was no such affection for James.

James knew he had to strike and strike now. This needed nipping in the bud before Miranda started drawing up a suitable wardrobe plan for a trip to Ireland.

"Today demands a double celebration," he announced. Bemused, the pair almost snapped to attention. "Buzz's win today, means that in total he has won enough prize money to make him eligible for entry to very special race. A race that only a select few horses are permitted to run in. It's in Switzerland, in February in St. Moritz. By that time of year, the huge lake has completely frozen and the horses race across the ice. The prize money, a healthy £23,000 and I reckon Buzz could do it."

He left the words to hang in the air for a second, to allow them to sink in. Taking a sip of his champagne, he then launched into full flow. "I've been before, when I was assistant trainer to John Hill, with a horse called Night Flyer. He came third and I was the one who trained him. I'm convinced Buzz has the ability and the disposition to run a good race there and you guys would love it. The skiing is plentiful and the bars are fantastic. Some of the biggest names in racing will be there. We're not just talking about rubbing shoulders with a couple of faces at Dunstall Park. This is a serious opportunity for you as owners, one you should be very excited about."

James was working hard, playing every card, every ace he had and it was hitting some serious hotspots with the pair. The prize money alone was more than Simon had offered to pay for the horse, a prospect for Alistair to digest slowly! Meantime Miranda imagined the scene; picturing herself, elegantly skiing down the idyllic mountainside by day and drinking alongside some rich sheik by night. Perfection!

"Few people have the privilege of owning a horse like Buzz. You can own racehorses all your life and not find one with the ability he has. Simon knows that and I would imagine he already has an owner lined up; someone intending to run Buzz, possibly even at St. Moritz in their own name. If they buy him now for £20,000 and were to win at St. Moritz scooping the £23,000, he has cost them nothing. All the hard work you guys have put into the horse would be for nothing. Someone else would get all the glory."

"Oh Alistair it does sound like fun doesn't it? We don't have to sell him do we? I would love to go to St. Moritz with Buzz. After all, we found him, didn't we? And he's my Buzz! Why should someone else have all the fun?" Miranda sidled up to Alistair, hanging off his arm as she waited for his response. She knew she would have her way and if she wanted to keep him, keep him they would!

"St. Moritz it is then!" Alistair raised his glass as he spoke. "Here's to Buzz," he toasted.

"Buzz!" they all repeated, knocking their glasses together in celebration.

3-0 and game over thought James!

James downed the remainder of his glass in one and placing his champagne flute deliberately onto the bar top, he breathed a huge sigh of relief. He visibly relaxed, shoulders dropping a tad, giving away the emotional rollercoaster of the day he had been subjected to. After the highs of Buzz's win and then the sheer panic both he and Clare felt in the face of losing the horse, altogether he was exhausted. He had managed to claw their position back from the jaws of defeat. He had to find Jonesy and put her out of her misery. He knew she'd be breaking her heart in the barn somewhere.

He didn't want to abandon Alistair and Miranda to their own devices but by the same token he didn't want them bumping into a very emotional Clare. She had no idea yet that he had saved them from potential disaster and could possibly say something she would later regret. Thankfully Alistair called time on the drinks session. They had plans with family later that evening and had a car booked to collect them. Thanking God for small mercies, James headed back for the barn.

The clanking of the stable doors opening and closing for evening stables duties, told James that Clare was skipping out the boxes. He found her in the end box, puffy eyed; she'd clearly been crying. Her nose was bright red from blowing it.

"How's your chest after he kicked you?" he asked.

"Oh I'm alright." Without looking up, she kept on with her task. Up and down went the fork, sifting through the bedding for muck. She couldn't bring herself to ask what the outcome had been. She was terrified to hear the news that Buzz would be sold and by this time she had convinced herself there would be no other end to the story. Clare knew what a money hungry man Alistair was and that Miranda was fickle. She was just as capable of buying and selling horses as quickly as she changed her knickers.

"You worry too much," James said, smiling.

Clare didn't see him smile and at that moment the emotion overtook her. The weeks of pressure, the gruelling work regime, the highs and lows of the wins and losses, Urban Myth's death and now finally the possibility of losing Buzz was just all too much.

"Worry too much? Are you blind? For God's sake man, what do you want from me? Blood? I come out here and graft my arse off for these horses. I give them my life. I put everything I have into them. Then in an instant, because I've done my end of the job well and got the horse winning, the likes of Simon blasts in and takes them away from me. Just like that! Gone James! Bloody gone! And who's going to look after him like I do, eh? All that trust. The time, work and hours and hours of effort all for nothing." So enraged was she, that spittle flew as she spoke and the vein on her forehead bulged, as she got more and more agitated. Finally awash with tiredness and despair she stopped and looked up.

"Feel better now?" he asked, still grinning.

"What's so funny?" Confused, she stood waiting for an explanation.

"For a start, you, when you're mad! He's not going anywhere that bloody Buzz! Well, except St. Moritz!" Relishing the moment, James stood, leaning against the stable doorway grinning inanely. He was feeling rightly proud of himself for saving the day.

"What? I mean, how do you know? Did you tell them about it? What did they say? What about Simon's offer?" She spluttered.

"That toffee nosed prat! I dispatched him quick, sharp. The temptation of St. Moritz then proved too strong for Alistair and Miranda. For him, it was the prize money that did it and for her, the social scene sold it."

"Hang on a minute. Are you telling me they're now on board? We're entering him, we are going and they are going to decline Simon's offer. Right?" After convincing herself she would have to part with Buzz, Clare was struggling to process the news that he would be staying after all.

"Yes Jonesy. That's what I'm saying. Now stop your wittering and get these boxes done. I fancy a drink. It is Boxing Day after all."

****

Buzz now fulfilled the criteria and was eligible to run at St. Moritz in the listed race that was the Grosser Preis, sponsored by American Express. However, it didn't stop there. Buzz needed to maintain his form. He had to run well between Boxing Day and the ballot, to secure his place in the race. When entering a race of this calibre, with the level of prize money on offer, there would almost certainly be more entries than there were places available. After all, you cannot have 50

horses running in one race. There were 11 places available to the entrants. Once the entries were in, there would then be a ballot. The ballot would be based on several factors; the prize money won during that season's races, the horse's form and the horse's rating would all be taken into account.

There are differing types of races that trainers enter horses for. At the lower end are 'Handicaps'. Then once proven in Handicaps, the next bracket up is 'Listed Races'

Buzz to date had been running in Handicaps. Races in which, horses carry different weights. A better horse will carry a heavier weight, to give him or her, a disadvantage when racing against slower horses. This gives all the runners an equal chance to win. Whether a horse is better than another horse is decided by that horses rating. This in turn is decided by their performance. The more placings and wins they achieve, the higher their rating becomes. Horses are rated separately on turf, all weather and over hurdles.

The closer the horse's rating is to the handicap mark of the race the more likely the horse is to be accepted for the race it is being entered for. For example, if a race has a handicap of 80 and your horse has a rating of 79, you are likely to be accepted during balloting over a horse with a rating of 70.

However the race in St. Moritz was a 'Listed Race'. These races are aimed at horses with a rating around the 80 mark. To be accepted in the balloting process, Buzz had to maintain his form and continue to run around this mark. After the Boxing Day win, his rating was 83. Although there is no handicap for comparison, Buzz's rating would affect the amount of 'weight' he carried during the race, should he be successful in balloting. The higher his rating, the more weight he would carry on the day.

There are two types of weight: 'live' and 'dead'. 'Live weight' is considered favourable over 'dead weight'. Live weight, is a jockey and his saddle; a flexible, movable weight. Dead weight is lead inserted into the saddle to disadvantage a better horse against a lesser rated rival. Dead weight is hard and inflexible and is considered heavier, although technically it isn't. Therefore the less dead weight a horse carries the better.

For all of these reasons Buzz had to keep running well to maintain his form: to keep him rated around 80 for, eligibility but not put him into the realms of too much dead weight if he qualified.

James planned to run him at Dunstall Park on the 13th and 31st of January in the hope of achieving this.

Clare and James were busy, busy! Although Buzz's entry was not yet confirmed, due to the magnitude of the journey and the task ahead of them, all plans had to be made as though the trip would go ahead. Not only did Buzz have to be ready, but arrangements needed to be made for travel, accommodation and staff cover in their absence. James liaised with the International Racing Bureau (IRB), informing them who would be travelling to St. Moritz and when. The IRB specialise in facilitating racing throughout the world. They arrange travel methods: in this case the ferry. They book and schedule flights for owners and trainers and arrange accommodation for horses and people alike, for the duration of the race meet and James considered them an invaluable source of help during the weeks leading up to their planned departure date.

Clare was the designated driver, Michelle her relief driver. They planned to set off for Dover, catch the ferry across the channel, drive across France to the Swiss border and from there, cross the mountains into Switzerland. The journey would take about 48 hours and it would be long and challenging for both horse and drivers. They planned to arrive with a few days to spare so Clare would have the opportunity to acclimatise Buzz and train him on the snow, utilising James' invaluable lessons learned with Night Flyer.

James would remain in the UK running the yard until the Friday before the race, which was due to take place at the end of the meet on the Sunday. He would then fly out to join Clare along with Alistair and Miranda. He would need to find staffing cover for the yard during his absence.

Clare was fretting over the drive. Buzz's travelling history wasn't exactly outstanding and it was the boat trip across the channel that concerned her the most. Once in the hold of the boat, Buzz would be alone in the lorry and she would be unable to attend to him. Banishing calamitous thoughts from her mind, she tried to focus her energy positively and concentrated on working out her route plan. James was insisting she learned how to fit snow chains on the lorry as he recalled an incident, on a cold snowy night on a Swiss mountainside, en route with Night Flyer.

"We were driving through the mountains on an extremely winding and steep road, the descent quite scary to be honest." He was laughing now as he imitated his driving position to Clare. "I was driving down the road, it was so bloody steep I might as well have been standing upright! My foot was down fully on the brake, we were sliding all the way, round the bends, slowly admittedly but that was irrelevant. I had no control at all!" James thought it was hilarious. Clare wasn't so amused. She had never driven abroad before, let alone in a horsebox with a precious load, through perilous mountain routes at night!

So, one bright and sunny January morning, Clare found herself sitting on a bucket, in the middle of the yard, watching Laurie Bell give a demonstration on how to fit snow chains to a lorry. Laurie had travelled with James and Night Flyer and they were borrowing his chains for the journey.

"All you do, is slip them round the tyre like this and clip them together," Laurie was saying as he fitted the first one. "Come on. You do the second one."

Struggling to lift the heavy chain onto the wheel but determined not to show it, Clare gritted her teeth and hauled for all her might. James was watching, getting irritated by Clare's lack of speed. James was a trainer, not a teacher, and patience was not his strong point.

"Come on Jonesy," he grumbled shoving her out of the way. "Look. Like this!" He got the chain over the wheel but couldn't master the technique of clicking it together. Getting increasingly more irritated the swearing commenced.

"Let me try again," said Clare, trying not to be too obvious in her amusement.

"No, no! Look! I've got it! Here. Look, that bit clicks in there. Uh, oh! Hang on. Not quite. Oh sod it! You do it!" and he threw the chain down in a huff and stood back, glowering.

"I was trying to do it seeing as it's me in the lorry and you on the plane." Clare raised her eyebrows and knelt back down to work, attempting to fix on the chains.

"Nothing changes does it Unett?" Observed Laurie. You did exactly the same thing in Switzerland, except, I seem to remember you were in such a bad temper, you burned your hand on the exhaust pipe!" Laurie laughed at James, who had started to see the funny side and in a rare moment of self-reflection, laughed at himself.

****

Buzz's run on the 13th came and went without event. He ran well enough, ridden by Dean and finishing 4th. There wasn't much room during the race. The horses were tightly packed and Buzz didn't get the opportunity to break out in front. He was sandwiched on the rail and it was fairly clear from early on that he wouldn't be able to break free from this position. James was happy with Buzz's run and Dean was pleased to be asked to ride him again. Dean was still bouncing after the win on Boxing Day, remembering the feeling of sheer power and ability he had got from Buzz in that race.

Clare had been so impressed with Dean's maturity and willingness to listen to her instruction on Boxing Day, that she had asked James if they could book him to ride Buzz at St. Moritz. James wasn't sure at first; concerned that Dean had no previous experience on snow. James reasoned that Buzz was new to the job and that at least half of the team should have some experience. Clare argued that Buzz would be well versed on how to run on snow by the time she had worked him for a few days. She was insistent that the experience was irrelevant. What was more relevant was the technique employed by the jockey. The wrong approach would render the whole thing a complete waste of time and money. Buzz had proven how capable he was of switching off and going backwards under such circumstances.

The second race was scheduled for the 31st January at Dunstall Park. Tigress had already won her race that day, so James was after the double. Dean was booked to ride again and on the day James agreed with Clare. If Buzz ran well again with Dean on top, then he would ask him to ride in St. Moritz.

They had been drawn 1 of 8, Buzz's favoured position on the rail. Dean was quiet and focussed that day and in the changing rooms he pulled Buzz's silks down over his head. With the cherry red silk on his hat, there was never a problem spotting Buzz from across the track. Weighing in for the race, he could hear the sniggers of two other jockeys waiting in line.

"Ha! Thinks he's got the magic touch, with that chestnut he won with on Boxing Day," spouted one.

"Luck more than anything. Shane says it's a pig of a horse," replied the other.

Refusing to rise to their jibes, Dean ignored them; instead thinking ahead to the race. Walking out to the parade ring, it took him no time to find Buzz. On form, he was dragging Clare around, kicking and snorting like a raging bull. Well, he's as ready as he'll ever be! Dean decided.

"Leg him up James. I'm struggling to keep this horse horizontal!" Clare barked at James, as she passed where the two men stood huddled together discussing tactics.

"You know the craic with him. He's ready to rock and roll today. Ride him in the usual way, head out in front, make all." James looked around and beckoned Dean closer. "We're taking him to St. Moritz to run in the listed race. Win today and you'll be the pilot."

Stunned, Dean's eyes lit up. "St. Moritz. You mean the snow races? Next month?"

"That's exactly what I mean. Now come on, let's get going before he drags Jonesy round the track on the end of that lead rein."

If Dean wasn't already focussed enough that day, what James had just told him certainly did the trick. As they cantered down to the stalls Dean could picture the scene: the snow covered lake, the huge towering mountains, the sun glaring down, as they thundered across the snow. Today he had to win.

The stalls flew open and Dean let him go. After just four strides, Buzz was ahead. The rail zipped by on Dean's left. He could hear the sound of the horses behind him but they weren't gaining. Buzz was flying! One step came effortlessly after the next. Faster and faster they went. Dean sat quietly, breathing in the cold air as it blasted his face, then in the blink of an eye they were rounding the last bend. Feeling Buzz stretch down and lengthen his stride, Dean knew the horse could win. Buzz knew he was nearly home and he wanted it. Hammering the final stretch, they won by a clear 2 lengths. Dean was reeling with excitement and had to double check with James that he hadn't dreamt it. St. Moritz and the snow races, on a horse like Buzz! It was the stuff of dreams!

"Yes you heard right," said James. "You've got the ride if you want it."

"Want it! Are you kidding? I'll walk there if I have to!" Dean's heart was about to burst out of his chest.

"Eh …. Dean, you have to get off and go and weigh in before you get a penalty!" Clare politely reminded him of his obligations.

"Christ! Yes, sorry. I'll get off," Dean muttered back in a trance. He was already planning his fitness regime, he needed to be as fit and ready as Buzz. He wanted to be unstoppable. Interrupted once more from his thoughts, he heard Miranda. The couple had not been able to make the race on the 13th as Alistair had whisked her away for a 'practice' ski holiday, in preparation for St. Moritz. So the day had come and gone without the melodrama of Miranda Cavendish. No such luck today. Dean certainly considered them the fly in the ointment!

"My Buzz!" She squealed as she reached up to pat him. Typical of people who are not familiar with horses, she tapped him on the nose rather too hard and startled him in the process.

"Well done lad!" Alistair said to Dean. "Well ridden."

"To be honest I didn't do much Sir. He's a great horse," replied Dean as he stripped off his race saddle and disappeared off to weigh in.

"Good job James!" Alistair moved on, enthusiastically shaking James' hand. "So pleased we could make it today, especially now he's won again!"

"We're glad too you could be here to see it. Aren't we Clare?"

"Oh, yes of course. So glad!" Clare almost spluttered the words. "James, I think that guy wants your attention. She nodded towards the 'At the Races pundit' who was approaching at speed. Almost before Clare had finished her sentence, there was a flurry of activity and James was swamped by media attention.

"Mr Unett, is it true you're planning on running Bressbee in St. Moritz, on the ice?" asked Bob Couper.

"Where did you hear that?"

"Mrs Cavendish told us earlier that you're planning on running him in the Grosser Preis on the 23rd February. Is that right? You've had the double today: first Tigress, now Buzz, and he's the horse you plan to take?" pressed Bob.

"Alright, alright! Yes we are. He's on form and running well with Dean Wellings on top, so we've entered for St. Moritz on the 'White Turf'," James relented. Now the racing world would know. More pressure to add to the already overflowing pot!

"Why there?" asked Bob.

"Three reasons:

One, because the prize money is excellent!

Two, because no British trainer has ever had a winner in the listed race, ……and…..

Three, because I have the horse to do it!"

Smiling, James thanked Bob for his interest and turned back to where Buzz, Clare, Alistair and Miranda were standing.

"The secret is out now! That'll get them talking!" laughed James. Sheepishly Miranda offered a rambling excuse for spilling the beans.

"Sorry James. I didn't mean to. I didn't realise who he was and before I knew it, I'd blurted it out! It's just that I was so excited with all the plans and arrangements and now today's win as well, that I just said it. I'm sorry."

Not wanting to dampen spirits, James laughed it off.

"No use crying over spilt milk. Like I said, it's done now. The cat's out of the bag!"

So the end of January had paved the way for February's events. Buzz was ready, the jockey chosen, the preparations for travel and accommodation made and the racing world knew their intentions. Now, only one more hurdle remained, the ballot. Hoping and praying for selection, James felt his stomach churn every time the office phone rang. The long awaited call finally came through on the 3rd February. Buzz had been selected and they were in!

Chapter 9

Woken from a fitful sleep, Clare reached over and silenced her alarm. 2.15am blinked the digital clock. 2.15am on Tuesday 18th February. It was time to take Buzz to St. Moritz.

The previous day had been a whirlwind of preparations. She had methodically loaded the lorry with: haylage nets, water tubs, grooming equipment, tack, rugs, feed, maps, supplies and the snow chains. The floor was covered with wood shavings to give Buzz something underfoot to help him grip and to soak up any little accidents he was bound to have during the 48 hour journey. She had checked and double checked the file with the official travel paperwork for Buzz and left it ready on the work surface next to her flask in the kitchen. His passport and hers were included in the bundle. Her bag was light and insignificant in comparison to the mountains of equipment needed for Buzz. It consisted of riding clothes: her hat, boots, body protector, one smart outfit and clean underwear. Buzz had a bigger wardrobe than Clare!

She planned to load Buzz and leave Dunstall Park in the early hours, then collect Michelle. Next they would head down to Dover and catch the ferry across the channel to Calais. The boat left Dover at 8.30am.

Clare was shattered after only managing a couple of hours sleep at best. That evening had been a long one. She had made all the necessary preparations in good time and was ready for an early night when Miranda and Alistair had arrived unprompted. Not wanting to be rude, James and Clare joined them for dinner at the Holiday Inn on the

course. The evening wore on and on and eventually Clare made her excuses and left James with them in the bar. She was completely preoccupied with the travelling. Having never driven abroad, being unable to speak French, German or Swiss and suffering a serious amount of pre-race nerves, Clare wasn't exactly the best company anyway! Couple that with a horse that wasn't known for his good travelling habits and a boat trip across the pond, it was fair to say that Clare was feeling a little pressured. She could not help herself from double checking Buzz's night rugs as she passed the barn.

As she straightened his fleece, Clare assured Buzz she would be with him every step of the way and that he wasn't to worry or fuss, she would look after him. Blissfully unaware of his early start or the road trip ahead, Buzz stood blinking in his stable as his sleepy eyes adjusted to the stable light. He looked at her wondering what he had done to deserve her late night visit. Satisfied that he was comfortable, she returned to the house for some well-earned shut eye. She had set the alarm and crawled into bed, falling into an unsettled and restless sleep.

Pulling on her fleece and jeans quietly so as not to wake James, she pulled the bedroom door closed behind her and tiptoed her way down the stairs. The enormity of her task was daunting. Worrying over Buzz and his journey she chided herself. She needed to be calm, composed and professional. She told herself that all the worrying in the world wouldn't get them to St. Moritz. Drawing a mental line under it all and focussing, she made up her flask then scooped up her bag and paperwork and headed for the door. Looking down, she could see Rascal sitting by the back door, ready as ever for a bit of late night rat catching!

"No Rascie, not tonight. Go back to bed. I don't need a stowaway!"

Making her way across the yard, the security lights blazed on glaring in her face. Shielding her eyes, Clare fumbled for the office door. Her plan was to open the lorry, get the side loading ramp down and ready then go in to get Buzz. The ramp groaned as it was lowered to the ground and Clare jumped in and swung open the partitions.

Back in the barn, Buzz and a couple of the others had heard her comings and goings and were standing with their heads over the doors craning their necks to get a better view of what she was doing. Deciding to settle them back down, Clare threw the nosey few, a slab of haylage each and then went about preparing Buzz. She would travel him in a tail bandage, to prevent him rubbing his dock on the side of the lorry and she would wrap his legs in travel bandages to prevent him from kicking his own legs, as he had done when he first arrived. His shoes had been removed earlier that week. James had suggested travelling him barefoot, with taped hooves, for added protection given his tendency to kick himself and the lorry. They had also started him on a course of Trimediazine, a low level antibiotic which is a race legal drug. It would keep him protected against any bugs he may be exposed to during his trip and keep him fit and healthy for the run.

Removing his stable rug, she threw on the travel rug and stood back to look at him. He looked very smart! The green bandages and rug complimented his bronze coat. He certainly looked every inch the racehorse but the nagging thought in Clare's mind was his sea legs not his racing legs!

Loading him was simple enough. Although bemused by his early morning adventure, Buzz walked up the ramp obediently and turned to be tied. He was certainly surprised to find two bulging haylage nets! When travelling locally racehorses wouldn't have haylage nets. On this occasion though, Buzz would be on the lorry until he reached their overnight stop outside Baden-Baden late that evening, some 16-18 hours later, so Clare had ensured he would have plenty to eat during the trip.

Lifting the ramp, Clare was once again dazzled by the security lights; illuminated as though she was in her own private stage show. While the rest of Dunstall Park slept soundly she started the engine. The lorry had a cut through cab so she could view Buzz easily as he stood in the back. She crept out of the yard, out of the gates and with her indicator blinking orange into the darkness of that February night she turned left out of the car park onto the road beyond. Next stop Michelle's house.

Drawing up outside, Clare could see the porch lights on. Up and ready for action, Michelle emerged from her front door. Smiling with excitement she skipped up the pathway, crossed in front of the lorry and hopped up into the passenger seat.

"Mooooorning!" she said to Clare with a school girl grin on her face.

"Mooooorning to you too!" said Clare. "You all ready?"

"As I'll ever be!" replied Michelle.

With that Buzz erupted in the back with his kick, kick, kick!

"I think he's ready too!" laughed Clare.

In high spirits they trundled off, onto the M6 motorway. By this time it was 3am. The boat left at 8.30am so they had little over five hours to get to Dover and onto the boat. The M6 blended into the M1, then the greater London ring road, the M25. This could be tricky, as Clare wanted to get around it and onto the M2 before the traffic built up in the early morning rush hour. They had allowed two hours to get themselves to the M25, bringing them on at approximately 5am. They then had 45 minutes on the M25 and another 1 hour 30 minutes along the M2 to Dover getting them to the dockside for 7.15am, a good hour before the boat sailed.

The uneventful trip along the M6 and M1 seemed long. They had swapped drivers half way along as Michelle had not driven the lorry before and wanted to have some experience on English soil before trying her luck in France and Germany! Upon reaching the M25 it became a different story. The early morning traffic was already building and by the time they reached the QE2 Bridge at Dartford, they were crawling at 15mph. It was still dark and it was drizzling. The wipers squeaked as they drew back and forth across the huge windscreen. They were losing time and Clare knew the boat wouldn't wait. Frustrated they sat in the stop, start traffic. Constantly checking her watch, Clare was getting very fidgety. Michelle was tapping her fingers on the wheel, willing the traffic to disperse. At 6.15am they finally peeled off onto the M2. The clock was ticking and Clare knew they were cutting it fine. As they motored through Kent and the sun came up Clare and Michelle, with their precious cargo, finally spotted signs for the docks.

Following the signposts they drove through a myriad of road systems that led over flyovers and down through tunnels. The industrial sized port was like a world alone. Complete with its' own road system and train line, it reminded Clare of some kind of science fiction land. They could see the loading cranes bolted to the dockside, the huge pieces of robotic-looking machinery were dormant but imposing, set against the grey drizzle filled sky. Seagulls perched on the top edges of the huge containers that the cranes had been shifting. Clare wondered what was in them and whether they were arriving or leaving British shores.

Hurriedly they pulled into the large car park that was the loading platform. It was 8.10am and they could see a huge ferry on the dockside. The 'roll on, roll off' type boat had its massive end dropped, butting up to the tarmac creating a driveway for passengers and their vehicles. The ferry was already loading when they arrived and they could see right into the bowels of the boat as lorries were being directed onto the ship. With no time to spare, they slipped into line behind an HGV and sat patiently waiting to load, like lemmings ready to jump off a cliff. They had made it just in time! Checking Buzz was quiet, Clare turned to find he was still working on the first haylage net, determined not to leave a scrap. He would look up alertly at the sound of a moving lorry or a dockworker's voice but always settled back to his haylage.

Winding down the window, Michelle passed the operator their boarding passes and Buzz's travel paperwork. Wrapped in waterproofs and barely visible under his hood, he glanced over them and waved her onto the ferry, pointing at the lane she was to take. Following the floor markings, they drove onto the ferry and down into the lower section of the boat along with the larger vehicles. They were guided over to the left side of the deck, where vehicles travelling with livestock were backed up next to the wall. This would allow the loading ramps to be opened and leant against the wall creating a through draught to prevent the animals overheating. More like an underground car park than a boat, Clare could smell the fumes from the vehicles. The noise inside the boat was amplified by the enclosed nature of the cavern-like hold. This was the part of the journey she was dreading the most; she had to leave Buzz alone on the lorry.

Usually the turning off of the engine would signify to Buzz that they had arrived at the races so when Michelle switched it off, he predictably hammered the side with his hooves impatient to get out. That wasn't today's plan. Clare was desperate to settle him as much as possible before she would have to leave him. Opening the ramp, she propped it against the wall, scooted back round to the jockey door and clambered inside to attend to Buzz. She first needed to strip Buzz's rug off as James had advised because the hold of the boat would become warm with the heat from the ferry's engines. They didn't want Buzz sweating up and losing valuable fluids in the process. She also needed to check his bandages, top up his haylage and offer him a drink. Dehydration on a long journey was always a danger and they needed

to minimise the risk so she added electrolytes to his water as a precaution.

In the back of the lorry he had stopped scoffing his haylage and was waiting somewhat impatiently for the ramp to lower fully. Instead Clare appeared through the jockey door. Buzz stood looking around, tilting his head to get a view of his surroundings through the opened ramp. He was listening to the strange noises; metal upon metal and the clanking and groaning of the ferry as it became fuller and fuller. Vehicles were loading above them now and as each one drove onto the ferry, the thud of the tyres passing over the loading platform was rhythmical and persistent.

Michelle had gone off to find the ladies. As she climbed up the thin metal stairs onto the passenger deck of the ferry, she could hear the banter of the French staff and passengers.

"Excuse me. Where are the ladies toilets?" she asked.

"Les toilettes sont ici Madam," replied the young porter pointing to the right.

That struck Michelle as strange, they usually spoke English.

Over the speaker system she heard more instructions for passengers, all in French. Recognising that the announcement was explaining that the ferry was about to set sail, she set off to drag Clare off the lorry and up onto deck.

"Come on. The boat's about to sail! We have to go up on deck Clare."

"Yes I know. I'm coming. Do you think he'll be OK down here? I mean, what if he starts panicking or gets sea sick or something?" The concern in her voice was evident.

"Look there's nothing we can do. He's fine at the moment. We might be able to sneak down later but we can't stay. They're checking through the vehicles now. Come on!" Michelle became insistent.

Reluctantly, Clare stepped aside and patting him gently on the neck assured him she'd be back to check on him. Buzz, wondering when he was going to be unloaded and a little confused, decided to voice his opinion with a sharp kick to the side of the lorry. He snorted in defiance. Completely torn, Clare forced herself to jump out onto the deck. She was sick with worry and apprehension. Leaving him to fend for himself went completely against everything she knew. She wanted to sit with him, talk to him and keep him safe.

She had been having a recurring dream that the ferry was caught in a storm and water was pouring into the hold. Buzz was stuck; tied fast and helpless in the lorry, waiting to drown as the water level rose around him. She knew in her rational mind that this wouldn't happen but walking up onto the deck and leaving him kicking in the lorry was one of the most emotional things she'd ever done. The firing up of the engines snapped her out of her day dream. The ferry powered up, lurched forward and they were moving. There was no going back now. They were on the ferry and they were going to sail across the channel with Buzz in the hold alone. A steward approached and ushered them up the stairs, showing his obvious annoyance at their lack of consideration for their own health and safety. When they reached the top, a ticket inspector asked for their paperwork. Rustling through her bag, Clare produced the file and handed it to the inspector. He sifted through it, seemingly searching for something.

"Do you know this is the French ferry boat?" he asked accusingly, in broken English.

"What do you mean the French boat? We are going to Calais right?" asked Clare.

"Yes, but this is the French boat, operated by Sienna. You are booked onto the English boat, the P & O ferry that docked in T5," he replied impatiently. "There is a French boat and an English boat. You are on the wrong ferry and I see you are travelling with a horse.... yes.... a Buzz..."

Feeling very small and silly, it dawned on Clare that in their rush to get to the ferry on time, they hadn't checked their tickets. They had just pulled up to the first boat they came to. It hadn't occurred to her that there was more than one boat.

"Well what can we do? We are moving!" said Clare pointedly.

"I will have to notify the authorities in Calais, as they may want to check your cargo and your Buzz."

"What do you mean check him? For what?" Clare was getting irritated. Her precious horse was alone in the lorry, doing god knows what and now she had to contend with this officious idiot. "Calais is Calais, no? What difference does it make? His paperwork is complete and accurate and we've paid for our ticket so what's the problem?"

"I don't know if there is a problem Madame. I will have to check. You have boarded the wrong boat," repeated the inspector. "I will notify you, before you disembark in Calais, of your instructions."

Michelle, sensing Clare's anxiety, attempted to distract her.

"Come on, we need breakfast. We've got a long drive on the other side. Let's get some people fuel!" She dragged Clare away towards the cafeteria. "What do you fancy? A bacon bap or full English?"

"I can't eat I feel sick. What if he goes over in the lorry? We won't know."

"Stop it! He's fine, just his usual kicking self. He'll settle into his hay again. Either way, you're no good to him half starved. Now choose something!"

The cafeteria was a small room; hot, stuffy and full of lorry drivers, all of whom were jabbering away in French. The girls ordered a breakfast each and sat at a table looking out to sea. They were moving, slowly but doggedly out into the channel. Clare could still just make out the looming white cliffs as they disappeared from view. The food was vile; watery scrambled eggs and shrivelled scraps of bacon. Clare wasn't particularly hungry before she entered the cafeteria and the quality of the food was doing nothing to entice her to eat. The sweaty, French lorry drivers thought it was most amusing having two pint sized English girls and a crazy horse on board and took it upon themselves to offer their 'services' should they be required. Surrounded by crass men and disgusting food, all Clare wanted to do was go below deck to Buzz.

"James won't be too impressed," giggled Michelle whilst slurping her steaming mug of tea.

"James probably isn't even out of bed yet!" Clare smiled. "I'm tired. I think I'll try and get an hour's sleep before we get frisked by the French authorities."

"Ooh la, la!" cooed Michelle in a fake French accent. "I'd like to see them frisk Buzz! He'd teach them a trick or two!"

They wandered out to the tired, shabby lounge area, politely declining the Frenchmens' services and huddled down for the short journey.

Before long a change in engine tone told the girls they must be approaching Calais. Clare jumped up, relieved that they had not been involved in a catastrophic ferry disaster after all and that the dream she'd been having night after night was just that, just a dream!

She hadn't managed to sleep at all but had sat counting down the journey time until she could get back to Buzz. Fast as a whippet she grabbed her bag and headed for the stairwell. Pushing through the queue, she didn't care who she offended in the process. Buzz was on her mind. Happy to grab an eyeful as they passed through the corridor, the lorry drivers stood aside allowing the girls to weave their way to the front of the queue. They artfully avoided the inspector as they did so.

The door was opened and down the stairs they went. Clare could see the lorry, exactly where she'd left it. Leaping through the jockey door, she found Buzz standing quietly resting his hind leg, chewing his hay like a beach ride donkey.

"Hello lad! To think I imagined you would have turned yourself inside out by now. You are a good boy!" Smothering him with kisses, the relief was like a dam bursting. They had made it. He was unharmed and by the look of it completely unfazed to boot. Buzz was proving James right at every turn. He was tough and resilient and had coped with the boat trip extremely well. Not a drop of sweat on him!

Swapping the haylage net for a fresh and full one and putting his travel rug back on, Clare turned her attention to the next phase of the journey. The time now was 10am. By the time they unloaded and got on the right road, it would be approximately 11am. They hoped the French port authorities wouldn't take umbrage at them boarding the wrong boat. They needed to be squeaky clean and polite and get out of Calais smoothly, without hold ups. Their route would take them across Northern France towards Strasbourg, then across the German border to a town called Baden-Baden. There, the IRB had arranged overnight accommodation with a German trainer based at the local course in Iffezheim. It was a 12 hour drive, which Clare and Michelle would share with Michelle taking the first stint.

Rolling off the ferry onto French soil, the horse box looked like a dinky toy compared to the HGVs surrounding them at the port. As they joined the file of traffic rumbling across the tarmac, French Customs were randomly selecting vehicles for scrutiny. Much to Clare's and Michelle's despair, two officials, in their immaculately pressed suits, made their way over to the lorry. In perfect English they explained they would need to check the paperwork and contents of the lorry.

Obligingly, Michelle pulled the lorry out of the queue and parked it in a side bay. Whilst one of the officials checked the documents, the

other asked Clare to open the lorry for further inspection. The inspection didn't last long. Put out by the interruption while tackling his fresh haylage net, Buzz lashed out double barrelling the lorry. The inspector, who clearly had no horse experience, flew out the side door like a man possessed. In his effort to get out as fast as possible, he missed the step and fell, landing in a heap on the car park! Desperately trying not to laugh, Clare helped him to his feet. He was crimson with embarrassment and quickly made his excuses, scurrying back to his office with his partner following in hot pursuit.

Clare and Michelle drove out of Calais at 11.20am laughing out loud at the silly man and his wet mucky trousers. Good old Buzz had put him in his place! They headed onto the A26 E17 to Reims, then the A4 E50 on to Strasbourg. Michelle loved Robbie Williams and had his single blasting out in the cab. 'I just wanna feel real love' was on repeat and they motored across France singing like a couple of school girls on a night out.

Normandy is a land of half-timbered farms and graceful old manor houses. Numerous rebuilt towns, victims of the massive bombings and vast war cemeteries were sobering reminders of the toll inflicted on France during two World Wars. The towns were quaint and petite and what struck Clare most was the cleanliness of the place. Even the poorer areas were clean and well kept. Staring out of the window and with Michelle driving, Clare eventually drifted off into a deep sleep. Shattered after the build-up to the journey on the boat and the long day they had already experienced, she needed to rest.

****

Back at Dunstall Park James had indeed got up late after his session with Miranda and Alistair the night before. He had been woken briefly when Clare left but only because Rascal had taken the opportunity to jump into the warm space Clare had just vacated and her cold wet nose had brushed his leg. The morning had been straight forward. Tuesdays were fairly simple, muck out and exercise. He had hired two temporary staff members to cover while he and Clare were away in St. Moritz. Three of his horses in training were being rested while they were away so the work load was a smaller. Less to ride out daily and with Buzz gone, it seemed like half a job. Ideal for James as apart from giving instructions to the new staff, his head was in the clouds thinking about Buzz. He wondered whether he was travelling well and if the boat trip had gone to plan but most of all he was looking forward to catching up with Clare by phone when she arrived at her over-night stop.

James had also arranged to meet Dean to talk through the arrangements and plan for the race. He wanted to give him as much advice and help as he could. Dean had never ridden on the 'White Turf' and there was an art to it; the kick back from the horses' hooves would be horrendous making visibility poor for both horse and rider. The feel for the surface also needed an explanation. Although it would shift a bit, Buzz would be wearing studded horse shoes to give him a better grip. James had also received the list of runners and this was causing him a little concern. The favourite was a huge black German horse called Zatoof. Having won the race the previous year he was the one to watch. Trained by Frau Mader, he was the highest rated horse in it, and he had experience on the ice. James hadn't mentioned it to Clare. He knew she was feeling the pressure about the journey and telling her didn't change the fact that Zatoof was entered. This meant that unlike Night Flyer, Buzz would have limited time to acclimatise to the surface and environment. James was banking on the relationship and trust Clare had built with Buzz to give him faith when she asked him to gallop on the snow track. James was following his gut instinct. He was sure Buzz would draw the confidence he needed from Clare and perform on this strange new surface despite the limited time available. James had also seen the resilience Buzz had shown since starting his training with them and was confident he would step up to the plate.

Prattling around in the background, Alistair and Miranda had asked him to book them some skiing while they were in St. Moritz. This he had dutifully done, purely because it meant having some time away from them during the trip. Since the official announcement, about the plans to take Buzz to St. Moritz, Miranda had been pestering him constantly about who would be there and what dress codes applied. On and on and on! James had politely reminded her twice that he was a racehorse trainer, not a social secretary but she wasn't taking the hint. He had to make it to Friday without strangling her and he was dreading the journey ahead with them. Buzz's race was scheduled for the Sunday afternoon; Alistair, Miranda and James were booked to fly out

on Friday morning from Birmingham Airport. They would fly to Zurich, catch the train to Chur, then jump on a connection to St. Moritz. The final section of the journey would be on a vintage steam train that winds its way into the mountains and down again into the St. Moritz valley. It was going to be a long week.

Chapter 10

The road was long and straight, a never ending expanse of tarmac cutting through the French countryside. Clare was back behind the wheel and it was Michelle's turn to get some rest. It was late afternoon and they were approaching the French/German border at Strasbourg after driving for nearly six hours. At the border check point they were required to stop and have the travel paperwork for Buzz stamped by the authorities. The paperwork held information on the loading time, departure time, date and address of the horse and the arrival time, unloading time, date and address of their intended final destination. There were two sets for each journey: one for the journey from Wolverhampton to Iffezheim, just outside Baden-Baden where Buzz would be unloaded to rest for the night, and another from Iffezheim to St. Moritz, his final destination. The return journey had the same paperwork but in reverse order. These papers had to receive an official stamp before the horse would be permitted to cross the border so Clare needed to find the border control office and obtain the stamp.

The night was drawing in as they approached the check point and Clare and Michelle could see what looked like the 'official' building. What they couldn't see was how to get to the building from the AutoRoute on which they were travelling. It was a lone circular building set into the hillside to the left of the road. Taking the next exit and paying the toll, they then wound their way back in the direction of the building. Clare and Michelle were bemused to find the place deserted. Unable to continue without the stamp they began walking around the exterior of the strange circular structure knocking on various doors hoping for a response. Finally an answer came from one of the offices; a small man, looking dishevelled and harassed, flung the door open. He stood staring questioningly at the girls awaiting some kind of explanation for their interruption.

"Sorry, err mm, excuse moi. We need a stamp, merci," spluttered Clare in the most ridiculously over done French accent.

"A stamp you say? Oui, door seven!" And with that he shut the door in their faces.

Falling about laughing at each other, the girls continued around the building until reaching door seven. They banged insistently on the wooden veneer until they heard a stirring from inside. The heavy door opened and in front of them stood the largest, most rotund man they had ever seen. His uniform was bulging at the seams and his bright red face made him look like the 'fat controller' from Thomas the Tank Engine. Struggling to remain straight faced after their fit of the giggles, the girls tried to explain as best as they could that they needed a stamp for Buzz's paperwork so they could continue their journey into Germany. Virtually rolling into the office, the girls followed behind him, where without speaking he perused the paperwork.

"Buzz..... le cheval...... Buzz....." he said.

"Eh, oui monsieur. Buzz, our horse," said Clare.

"St. Moritz, votre cheval est un cheval de course?"

"I think he is asking about him being a racehorse," guessed Michelle.

"Oui, un cheval de course," nodded Michelle in agreement.

"Est-il bon?" he said smiling now.

"Good? Yes! He's the best! I mean oui, il est le meilleur!" Michelle was getting into her stride. When discovering she was included in the plan for St. Moritz, she had done some refresher language sessions with her French hairdresser back in the Midlands. Most of which included vocabulary that would be required for discussions regarding the horse. "He is the best" had been perfectly practiced.

Pulling his wallet from his pocket the man handed Clare forty Euros. Taking it Clare laughed.

"I will place the bet for you and bring your winnings back next week! Eh, Tuesday. How do I say "Tuesday Michelle?"

"Mardi."

"Oui Mardi!" the man said smiling. Looking very pleased with his good business, he stamped Buzz's papers and showed the girls to the door.

"Bon Voyage," he called after them as they headed back to the noisy lorry in the car park. Buzz was sick of waiting! Kick, kick, kick!!!

The actual border was some way off so onward they plodded, flagging now and looking forward to reaching their overnight stop.

Baden-Baden is a spa town very close to the border in Baden-Württemberg, Germany. It is located on the western foothills of the Black Forest, on the banks of the Oos River in the region of Karlsruhe. Just outside Baden-Baden is the international racecourse in Iffezheim. The racing calendar on the turf track starts with the Spring Meeting, followed by the Grand Festival Week and rounded off by the Sales & Racing Festival. A local trainer based near the track had offered Buzz overnight accommodation in his stables. The IRB had forwarded some hand written directions and the girls were concentrating hard on following them, so hard that they didn't notice the fuel gauge until it started blinking red at them. Michelle was back in the driving seat and she alerted Clare to the problem. So the search was now on for a petrol station at 10pm on a Tuesday night, on the road to Baden-Baden. With every mile, the gauge dropped lower. Running out of fuel with Buzz on board was not an option. Clare was failing to see the funny side by now, her tiredness making her irritable.

"This isn't funny you know, what are we going to do if we run out?" she said.

"Don't worry, we won't run out. Besides if we do we can ride Buzz to the petrol station!" Michelle jested.

Staring ahead stony faced Clare didn't respond to the joke. She was not finding their predicament funny at all. Still no sign of a petrol station, the road wore on into the night. Mild panic had just started to set in when finally, in the distance, Clare spotted a welcome sight. The illuminated sign shone brightly against the night sky. The 'SHELL' petrol station appeared like an oasis to the girls!

Refuelled and back on the road they continued their journey. They crossed the River Rhine over a huge metal bridge, before arriving at a large roundabout which was technically the French/German border. Here they were to take a right and start following signs for the race course. The signs had white horses on them which the trainer had hand drawn for them on their instructions. They were to drive through the village of Iffezheim and when they reached the high street, take the second right down a narrow street. That street was a cobbled residential street. The glowing street lights gave it a warm and appealing look; against the painted render of the buildings Clare could see the quaint homes. Iffezheim was an old German town dating back to the 1400s and it showed in the architecture. Due to the town's location on the

banks of the River Rhine, it had been a centre of commerce for many years. As they passed through the streets, Clare could see what once would have been old taverns and coaching houses. The place was steeped in history. Timber beamed property was everywhere and was now mostly converted into residential housing with a clear pride taken in the upkeep and care of the homes. It was spotless.

Bumping across the cobbles into the yard, Clare was relieved to see the stabling coming into view. As promised, in the corner of the small courtyard was a box with a light on. Buzz's box. Although safely at the stop point, her work wasn't yet done. She still had to attend to Buzz. Tired from travelling, he didn't bother kicking at this stop. Clare was keen to be able to unload him and let him stretch his legs before tucking him up in his bed. Again, electrolytes were added to his water and antibiotics added to his feed. Meantime, Michelle skipped out the back of the lorry, removing the dirty bedding and replacing it with clean for the journey the next day. Just as Clare was rugging him up for the night, a voice piped up,

"Evening ladies. I'm Patrick." Introducing himself politely, a man walked across the courtyard. "I live in the caravan on site and keep an eye on things round here. We have dinner ready for you so come over when you are ready." He pointed towards a small caravan tucked behind the stables.

It was gone midnight and Clare and Michelle were famished. They hadn't wanted to stop and eat, preferring to soldier on and the get the journey done. It was only now that they realised how hungry they were. The last meal they'd eaten was the dodgy food on the ferry so they were hoping for a better one here!

For the next two hours, they were entertained by Patrick and the trainer Franz. It turned out that Patrick performed drag acts on stage; his caravan was decorated with photographs of him performing. As if their journey wasn't already out of the ordinary, the girls found themselves enthralled by the wild stories and adventures of Patrick the drag queen. Apparently he was very good at his chosen vocation! He was also very good with the horses, he had been involved in the racing industry for years and had previously been a box driver based in Newmarket. Finally Patrick had settled in a caravan in Iffezheim on his friend's yard. The girls heard stories of fun and frolics at Iffezheim race track and the neighbouring pubs and clubs, eventually crawling from the caravan at nearly 2am. Shattered, but fed and watered, they headed for their beds. Clare could have sworn she heard Buzz snoring in his box as she crossed the courtyard.

6.00am on Wednesday the 19th, the girls and Buzz had an early start. Advised to get to the Swiss border early to avoid a hold-up, they managed only four hours sleep before the last push to St. Moritz. Although understandably hesitant to load, Buzz freshly bandaged and rugged walked up the ramp again. Next stop, the Swiss border.

Arriving at the check point there was little traffic and the border police checked and stamped the paperwork with typical German/Swiss efficiency. Before they knew it, they were into Switzerland with the final eight hours in front of them. The AutoRoute seemed a long way off as the lorry wound its way south toward Zurich, then across to Chur. They chugged along relentlessly on the two way roads, only stopping to refuel and grab a sandwich to go. Buzz by now was resigned to travelling;

Clare frequently looked over her shoulder and called through to Buzz letting him know she was still there. Reassured by her voice, he contentedly nibbled at his haylage. By mid-afternoon, they had started the mountain climb. They were now down to the last fifty miles which would take approximately two hours.

The road in front of them carved its way through the mountains, winding higher and higher with each turn. Covered in snow, the towering peaks stood impressive and breath-taking against the brilliant blue February sky. The sun shone down on the three travellers making their passage a feast for the eyes. Stunned by the beauty, the girls were quiet, soaking up the beauty of their surroundings. Below them lay huge lakes. At this point in their journey, they were driving at fairly low altitudes and the lower lakes were not frozen. The dark expanses of water were framed with fir trees and topped by the panoramic summits, a far cry from the views at Dunstall Park.

Up and up they went, reaching higher and higher into the ranges. The snow cover was getting more consistent now with the road clear but the sprinkling on the ground to either side thickening the higher they went. Now the lakes they were passing were frozen with a bank of snow building up on the roadside. St. Moritz itself lays in a valley deep in the Eastern Alps, home to the tallest summit in the Alps. In the bowl of the valley lies the lake, which at this time of year would be

frozen but in the summer months would have been and continues to be a vibrant place of religious note. Named after Saint Maurice, a Roman Catholic Saint, Pilgrims travelled to Saint Maurice to the church of the springs where they drank from the blessed waters in the hopes of being healed. Clare had read that in the early 1500s, the Pope at that time had promised full absolution to anyone making a pilgrimage to the church of the springs. She could imagine the harshness of that pilgrimage and the determination it would have required from those vulnerable souls, crossing the Alps in search of their absolution. They deserved absolution after such effort thought Clare. Laughing to herself, she didn't want absolution but a hot bath and maybe a winner would be good!

Passing through several tunnels they climbed the last of the peaks. The roads were quiet and it was so very silent apart from the hum of their little lorry echoing in the vast range: white brilliance lay all around with drifts banking up against the trees and rocks dotted along the edge of the road. As they began their descent into St. Moritz, the road became more treacherous. Dug into the mountain itself, jagged rocks lay scattered to the left with a vertical drop plunging to the right. Driving on the right meant the perilous drop was on the driver's side in a right hand drive lorry. Clare was driving by this time and with every turn and passing vehicle she held her breath. There seemed to be just enough space but not an inch more and the pathetic yellow and black barrier to her right offered her little solace. She was also aware that the windy nature of the travel would be hard on Buzz's tired bones. She could see him leaning on the partitions as they rounded corners, trying to support himself as they motored on.

James had warned her about this section of the journey. So far the girls had been lucky weather wise but when James and Laurie had travelled this very road with Night Flyer, things had been altogether different.

The night before their journey, heavy snow had fallen and the road had remained uncleared. Black ice and thick snow lay in wait around every bend. James remembered making the decision to stop just outside the mouth of a tunnel to fit the snow chains. This enabled oncoming drivers to see them more clearly as the tunnel mouths were straighter than the road itself, which continually wound round and down into St. Moritz. In freezing conditions, Laurie and James had struggled to fit their chains, their gloves making the fiddly clips difficult to attach. The biting cold however made it impossible to be outside for any length of time without them. James also burnt his hand on the exhaust pipe as he attempted to fit the offside front chains: his hands had been so cold he hadn't realised until the burn was fairly deep. They had continued their journey downwards, in what James had described as impossible driving conditions. The road was so steep in places, he had virtually stood up in the cab with his foot on the brake and used the lowest gears for the duration of the descent. At times he had recalled not feeling in any kind of control of the lorry and merely feeling like a passenger, as the lorry slipped and skidded down the road. With each bend he had closed his eyes expecting to hurtle off the edge. In places the snow had started to fall again and when driving through the flurries, visibility had been non-existent. To counteract this problem, the Swiss erect guides: red and white poles placed either side of the carriageway, with string attached to the tops which hang over the road. This provided an invaluable aid to James, Laurie and Night Flyer as they had been the only indicator of the road direction as they slipped and slid their way down the mountain. This was the only section of the journey that had concerned James, which was the reason he had been so insistent that Clare learned to fit the snow chains before they started the journey. He felt that the chains had prevented them having a serious accident on their journey and provided the vital lifesaving grip that had enabled them to steer safely off of the mountain and down into St. Moritz.

Michelle was gawping at the gigantic icicles hanging from every rock, crystal stalactites, hanging like Swords of Damocles, threatening to splinter at the top and crash down towards the road below. As night closed in, they finally completed their ascent and began their downward journey, snaking and weaving into the St. Moritz valley. The girls finally spotted lights sparkling in the night glinting like little beacons, beckoning them closer and closer with every twist of the road.

Clare's instructions were to meet Christen Von de Reck, another German trainer who would assist them in parking the lorry and guiding them to their hotel and stabling. The town is a centre for sports; water sports in summer and snow sports in the winter. All the sports are based on the lake so it didn't take them long to find their way to the trackside. The huge lake, frozen and covered in snow, was visible because of its

blank nature. Surrounding it against the black sky were the lights of the town and then a vast nothingness, a blank space. That was the lake: the racetrack. Their journey was over. They had arrived.

****

Waving furiously from his 4x4, Christian extended a warm welcome to the weary travellers.

"Welcome! I was beginning to think you had fallen off of the mountain road!" he jested.

"I'm surprised you couldn't hear us screaming as we came round the bends. Did the Swiss not think of just digging through the middle of the mountain? It would have been a much easier route!" Clare quipped back.

"Maybe, but it would not be as much fun! Over there in the corner, put the lorry over there," he said, pointing to their final resting place! Switching off the engine for the final time, the girls smiled at each other, their epic journey completed, safe and on time! Visibly relieved, they prepared to unload Buzz and give him his first taste of this very different environment. The car park was covered in crunchy snow!

Gingerly inching down the ramp, slightly stiff and only half awake, Buzz emerged from the lorry. As his hooves met the snow, he hesitated for a second and looked. Then without further ado he stepped forward and strode across the car park.

"Well, well, well, this is Bressbee eh! The English horse. Bressbee, he can run on the ice can he?" Clare didn't appreciate the patronising tone but knowing how trainers like to wind each other up she ignored Christian's taunts.

"He can run Christian! He can run and he loves it!" Giving nothing else away, Clare patted Buzz and chirped away in her usual style. She then led him past an array of lorries, some big, some small, some with foreign plates and some without making their way across the car park to the race stabling.

"I'm so proud of you," she hummed to him. "You travelled better than I ever imagined. I told you it would be fine. All that silliness wasn't needed at all and you've proved it. You're my star boy Buzz, you really are." His left ear was cocked, listening to her soft, gentle tone, his right ear pointed forward listening for sounds coming from up ahead. Buzz stuck to Clare like glue as his bulk crossed the dark car park, his hoof beats muffled by the snow and the crisp crunching of her foot falls breaking the silence of the night.

Christian showed them down a sloped walkway into the stables. They were slightly lower than ground level and accessed through sliding doors, which remained closed to keep the cold out, were two lines of boxes, five on each side. It was late. The grooms had long retired to their beds and the barn was quiet. Horses stood dozing in their boxes under the dim glow of the wall lights. Buzz could feel the cold against his tired skin and was glad to get inside his allocated box. Christian left Clare to her work and as she undid Buzz's head collar, he sank to his knees to have a long awaited roll in his thick straw bed.

Regimented in her care of him, she topped his water with the electrolytes and gave him antibiotics with his haylage and feed. Removing his hoof tape and leg bandages, she explained to him that he would be staying here for a while.

"I know it's a bit strange, this barn being a bit underground but it's just for a few days. Tomorrow you will get a good look around but for now you need to rest. I will be just up the road in a hotel, not far away my lad. Not far away."

Looking up, Clare noticed the stabling had internal exposed pipework running across the ceilings. The heat generated from them kept the chill from the horses in the -25ºC temperatures that could be expected at night. Putting Buzz's third layer of rugs on for the night, she knew he would be feeling the cold, especially after his long journey. After all, she was freezing herself!

In the box next door to Buzz, loomed a magnificent black thoroughbred. His beautiful onyx head hung over his stable door, eying up the latest arrival. "Zatoof," Clare read from the name card on the door. "Hello boy. You're handsome aren't you?" Disinterested in Clare, he stared intently at Buzz who was far too busy exploring his new box to be bothered. What Clare didn't know, as she admired the horse, was that he was the competition; last year's winner of the Grosser Preis and a formidable opponent.

Buzz sniffed his way around his accommodation, digging up his bed and nosing through his haylage. He slurped down a long and refreshing drink and stuck his head over the door surveying the barn. Whickering to the other horses in an equine introduction, he spotted

Zatoof next door. Craning over the door to get a better look, he pricked his ears forward and called to him. Zatoof, pretending he hadn't noticed Buzz's attempt at conversation, slipped back into his box and sighed heavily as though bored with the evening's events. Snubbed by the big black horse, Buzz found his attention wavering and went back to his haylage. Clare left him happily half munching and half dozing.

Christian dropped the flagging girls and their minimal luggage off at their hotel. Bidding them good night, he told them where he would be staying in case of any problems and drove back out into the night. The accommodation was a small chalet style block designed for skiers. Having easy access to the nursery slopes, it was located at the base of the mountain which also made it within easy reach of the lake. As they wandered down the deserted corridor looking for their room, a door opened and much to the girl's delight, revealed an extremely dishy ski instructor. Tall and muscular, his sun kissed skin complimented his blonde hair and blue eyes. Smiling at them as he strode past, the girls blushed and giggled. Quoting their favourite Robbie Williams number, 'I just wanna feel real love,' Michelle sang the strap line loudly enough that the ski instructor turned and laughed. Bordering on hysterical laughter themselves, they fell through their hotel room door like a couple of sweet sixteen year olds!

The room was incredibly basic, designed for inhabitants expected to be on the slopes all day, not particularly comfortable, with bland décor. The dated bathroom was clean but well worn. Cheap toilet paper and rough towels had been provided but soap was a stretch too far in this hotel and Clare resorted to scalding, hot water to clean the horse related dirt from her hands. Michelle wasn't impressed at all, complaining about the hardness of the mattress and the smell of the bed linen. The curtains were frayed at the edges and the carpet threadbare. Not exactly a home from home but it would serve its purpose.

"Oooh, look at those beautiful curtains!" said Michelle sarcastically. "Classy eh?"

"You would have thought they could have found something a little more up market than this surely."

"It's not great but to be honest I am so tired, anything will do. Besides, at least the neighbour is good to look at!" chuckled Clare.

It wasn't long before the complaints died down and tiredness took over. Curling up on their beds, the girls chatted over the events of the journey. The sense of relief was overwhelming. They had driven for two days, crossed the English Channel and two European borders and had done it in a horse box with a horse on board!

Closing her eyes Clare drifted into a deep sleep. With no energy left to think about what the coming days would hold, she did not dream of sinking boats or drowning horses. In fact she did not dream at all. Her head had switched off as she sank into oblivion.

Chapter 11

Friday 21st February 2003

Standing, watching, intrigued by the small coloured dots whizzing down the mountain, Buzz looked out across the landscape, through the window of his box. Although the stabling was set just below ground the windows were built into the top of the walls from the stable side allowing the horses some natural light and a view to die for. Buzz had no experience of skiing and found the picture postcard image in front of him very interesting! He hadn't had the best night. Aware of the - 25*C temperature that could be expected at night, Clare had rugged Buzz accordingly and although she'd spotted the heating pipes, had not realised to what extent they warmed the barn. Within an hour, Buzz was sweating! So in normal Buzz style, he had undressed himself. This strip tease had involved thrashing around, rolling and kicking until the belly and leg straps had torn at the seams. He then artfully clenched the shoulder gusset in his teeth and pulled the rugs forward. Dropping his head down, he then shook and rubbed on the stable wall until the rugs were far enough forward that their own weight made them slip over his head. Triumphant, he then proceeded to poo and wee all over them, just to ensure the point was rammed home when Clare arrived to see to him the following morning!

Having left Michelle in bed, Clare found Buzz standing idly gazing out of the window at the skiers with his rugs trashed and dirty on the stable floor. Chastising herself for not realising it would be a fully heated barn, she set about the morning routine. Added to that routine would be a call to James, to tell him she needed some extra rugs brought over for the journey home! Familiarising herself with the barn in daylight, Clare found the tools for mucking out and the storage area for tack and feed. Once her chores were complete, leaving Buzz to eat his breakfast, she made her way to a phone box to make her call. Tired from the journey, she had forgotten to charge her mobile and she knew James would be desperate for news. It had been too late to call the night before and she needed to let him know she had arrived safe and well, albeit minus a few rugs!

James answered the office phone after just a few rings, "Hello, Clare". He had been up bright and early to do his final jobs before leaving for St. Moritz later that morning. He had been listening out for the phone as he was keen to hear news of the journey. The minute he heard it, he dashed across to the office and grabbed the receiver. The hour time difference made it 6.45am UK time, no one else would be calling the office that early on a Friday morning!

"Hi! I thought you might have been riding out. You OK?" she asked.

"Yeah sure. You OK ? I tried to call you but I couldn't get through, are you all alright? How was the trip? Did he behave well?"

"He's fine. Travelled like a pro. Not a bother at all but he's trashed his rugs. You'll have to stick at least one in your bag and bring it over and I forgot to charge my phone but it'll be ok later." Feeding the call box with more Euros, she fumbled in her purse, her gloves making it impossible to grip the coins.

"OK, that's fine. Everything alright there? Did you meet Christian?"

"Yeah, he was nice. Pointed us in the right direction last night. Listen, I haven't got long. I've got to meet the farrier today and the vet will be here at some point to check the papers and passport. I'm going to lead him out this morning and then all being well, ride him out before dark tonight. You happy with that?"

"Crack on. We only have tonight and tomorrow and that's it, so get him acting on the surface. There's no time for resting back. He's got to get into the zone and fast." Wishing he was there, the tone of James' voice was firm and Clare could hear he sounded tense. "Is Zatoof there?"

"Yes. Next door. Big black horse. Why?" She was running out of

coins and time.

"Last year's winner. Try and work upsides him, he'll give Buzz a good lead."

"Oh right! Bloody hell! Last year's winner and he's declared again. Great! No pressure then!"

"Oh, just crack on will you and call me later. We're leaving in an hour. Snow shoes Clare. Remember he needs snow shoes and the second bend is sharp!" Click! The line went dead; she had run out of change. Hanging up the receiver, she left the call box and crossed back to the barn. "Zatoof," she said out loud.

Shuffling along the snowy pavement, she looked up at the scenery. She had never been in a place with such panoramic views. In the shape of a bowl, the now frozen lake formed the centre piece and the enormous peaks towered all around as though standing on guard, watching the comings and goings below. St. Moritz was just waking up and the hum drum of the day had started. Although it was daylight, the huge mountains shadowed the valley, preventing the sun from shining directly in, until around 10am when it was high in the sky. Clare planned to have Buzz shod by the resident farrier and get the vet checks done before leading him out in hand, onto the snow, all before lunchtime. She wanted to stretch his legs after the travelling and also let him gain balance and confidence on the surface before he had to do it carrying her weight. He had been worked on the snow at Dunstall Park whenever they'd had the opportunity but this was different. It was pure snow, deep and crispy with an underlay of ice, not like the pathetic sprinkles that fall back in the UK.

Getting her bearings, Clare could see that the stables were located to the north east of the lake. Directly in front of them, the polo arena, another prepared snow surface which hosted a fortnight of polo games annually. The last event had taken place the week before. It was a large rectangular area, fenced off with rails and she could see a man driving a machine across the surface, back and forth like he was mowing a lawn. Crossing the road to get a closer look, she could see that where he had driven the snow was compacted making it smoother and firmer. That would mean they could work more safely. Although the snow would still sink beneath your feet, it would be sticky rather than slippery and she hoped this would help Buzz gain confidence quickly.

Beyond the polo arena Clare could see a huge expanse of whiteness, accessible by crossing a small wooden bridge linking the arena to the track. Under the bridge gurgled a brook, running off the mountain this water was not frozen. It was one of the many springs that fed the lake, a trickling reminder that under the expanse of frozen ice there really did lay a huge lake. The ice started to form about three metres in from the bridge, crackling and porous at the edges but solid and strong the further inwards it crept. The lake seemed endless. It stretched as far as she could see and the edges blurred into the snow covered slopes beyond. Within the vast space lay the track. The 'White Turf' was a 'P' shape with a long straight, stretching out towards the south. The track then turned to the right, round a bend leading to a short straight and then right again re-joining the original straight, about three quarters of the way along. The finishing post was back on the straight, directly in front of what Clare had heard James describe as the 'tented village'. The 'tented village' was an area on the banks of the lake for the race goers and spectators. A huge grandstand, now empty, stood looking down on the track. Surrounding it were several white tents in which were bars, betting facilities and restaurants for the many guests. Behind the grandstand and central to the tents, lay the parade ring and the saddle enclosure, placed in prime view for the rich and famous. Due to the nature of the valley, Clare had a clear view of all her surroundings as it nestled in the dip, layering upwards. She could see the town above, with houses and apartments sitting one row above the next climbing up the mountainside. Framed by the peaks it looked like a toy town, in stark comparison with the raw and awesome splendour of the mountains themselves.

Arriving back at the barn, Clare found the vet inspecting Buzz. One job done, thought Clare. He scrutinised the paperwork and Buzz's passport giving Clare the all clear on both fronts. The farrier was booked for 9am. He arrived promptly and Clare led Buzz from his box to be shod. She had removed the tape from his hooves the night before, so his hooves could breathe and once he was shod with snow shoes he would be fit to go for a walk in hand. Snow shoes are very similar to regular horse shoes and are fitted in the traditional way, the difference being, three pieces of welded metal that protrude from the shoe; one at the front and one on either side. They are attached to the outside of the shoe and are approximately an inch long; the metal would add height, like studs on a pair of football boots. The welded metal pieces are designed to bite into the snow giving the horses more grip when working on the snow. Keen to explore the new barn and meet the occupants, Buzz wasn't keen on standing still for the farrier and required much pushing, shoving and calming from Clare until he was the proud new owner of his first pair of snow shoes.

Mid-morning in the barn was a busy time; the horses had eaten breakfast and were ready for work. Inside the ten occupants watched over their grooms as mucking out, sweeping and tack cleaning took place. One by one they went about their business, preparing their horses for exercise. Some were thoroughbreds, others polo ponies awaiting trips home after the end of the tournament.

It was time to take Buzz for a walk. Having sussed the lay of the land and checked out the polo arena, Clare decided she would take Buzz in there. She had watched the surface being prepared and knew it was a good enough place to start. After Buzz's performance with the farrier, Clare knew he was feeling fresh following journey so a chifney bit would be a sensible bet. Not knowing how he would react to his new environment, she didn't want him careering off across the lake if the mood took him!

It was just after 10am and the sun was creeping over the peaks, the rays spliced across the sky creating beams of light that shone down onto the arena. It was dazzling and both Clare and Buzz needed a minute to let their eyes adjust as they walked out from the relative darkness of the barn. Seemingly oblivious to the snow, Buzz jogged next to Clare. Quite limber after his journey, he swished his tail and kicked; enjoying the fresh sharp air he was alert and very alive. Clare loved him like this. He seemed to grow into an 18hh horse, strapping and vibrant as he danced across the road into the arena. Thankfully it was still empty. Clare intended to walk around the outside of the arena for a good 20 minutes and depending on his reaction, go out onto the track. She was so busy holding onto Buzz that Clare didn't notice Michelle standing by the rail.

"Good morning Clare. Nice horse. Who is he then?!" she joked.

"Oh, good morning sleepy head. How are you doing today? Gotten over the hard pillows yet?!" Clare teased back. The horse? You mean you don't know who this is? Why this is Bressbee, The Ice King!" Clare giggled as she was dragged past Michelle. Buzz wasn't hanging around; enjoying his walk he powered along. "I could do with some skis, then he could pull me around out here!" Clare shouted back.

Ducking under the rail, Michelle, dressed in a snow suit and matching hat, crunched through the snow after Clare and Buzz.

"What's the plan for today boss?"

Having memorised all the tips she had been given for the trip, she knew the lorry needed attention daily. The freezing temperatures could affect the engine and cause the diesel to freeze. Michelle needed to drive the lorry for at least 30 minutes every day if they were there to keep it ticking over. Laurie had warned Clare not to be negligent, as frozen diesel created a significant problem and was an expensive one to fix.

"Can you take the lorry for a drive, warm it up and skip it out if it's dirty? This idiot trashed his rugs last night, so if you see an equestrian shop, we need rugs! He's a 6ft 6, oh and please plug my phone in and charge it will you? The travel adaptor is in my bag. James was trying to get me but its dead."

"No problem. What are you doing now? He seems fine after the drive. Are you riding him today?"

"He looks fine doesn't he? Not stiff or sore. A tough nut this one. Yes, I'm going to walk him out for half an hour, probably onto the track then I'll ride later this afternoon. James and the owners will be here later, about 6ish," Clare answered in a matter of fact way. In truth, she couldn't wait to get on him. She had dreamed of flying across the ice like a windsurfer on the water and that dream wasn't far from reality now. The only question was whether Buzz had had that same dream. Would he run on the ice or would he hold back? There was only one way to find out and all would be revealed today.

Leaving Clare to walk Buzz around, Michelle returned to the lorry. As she crossed the road a strange site pulled into view. A bright bay horse was trotting along pulling a cart but instead of wheels it had skis. This was to be their first experience with 'Skijoring', another of the equine winter sports that took place on the white turf.

Clearly having had the same idea as Clare, the horse and ski cart pulled off the road into the arena. Save for the crunching of hooves through the snow, it moved silently sliding across the snow like a sledge. Clare heard the approaching horse's hooves and not wanting to get Buzz anymore on his toes than he already was, she kept walking. This was a sign to Buzz that there was no need to change pace or be

alarmed by the approaching horse. What she didn't know, was that attached to the horse was a peculiar looking cart and sitting on the cart was a driver dressed in colourful ski wear, goggles and a hat!

The skijoring pair trotted along the rail and came level with Buzz on his inside, with Clare sandwiched between the skijoring horse and Buzz. From the corner of his eye, Buzz spotted the cart and instantly spun around, dragging Clare backwards in the process. Desperately searching for a firm foot hold, Clare hung on to him for dear life as she felt him tense, preparing to flee from the terrifying cart. Offering calming words she managed to regain her composure. Holding him firm, she let him watch the spectacle as it made its way round the arena again. With no consideration for the obvious upset he had caused, the driver came at them again. Having never seen anything like it before and having this silent contraption heading straight at him again, was more than Buzz could handle. Panicked and trying to flee, he half reared but restricted by the chifney, he kicked instead. Bucking with one movement and striking out in anger with the next, he exploded on the spot.

"Whoa there lad. Steady now. Settle down Buzzer."

Clare knew she would only be able to hold him safely for a short while, with the slippery surface under her, she didn't have the best chance at staying vertical herself. She needed to get him out of the arena and the bridge over to the track provided the nearest escape route. Turning him towards it, she could see Michelle rushing over to her aid. Michelle was shouting abuse at the skijoring man as she skirted the edge of the arena.

Clare kept Buzz walking over the wooden bridge and out towards the track, eyes rolling and mouth salivating he looked like a rabid dog.

"Are you alright?" panted Michelle. "I passed him on my way over but didn't realise the idiot was going to come right up behind you like that. What an idiot!"

"We're fine. What the hell is that thing? I thought it was just a horse, didn't realise it had a cart on skis behind it!"

Headed for the rails on the right, Buzz had decided he'd put enough distance between himself and the seriously scary, skijoring fella and started to look ahead and walk in a relatively straight line. "I'll take him up past the stands and back again. You can go back. I should be OK now."

"OK, try not to lose him will you!" Michelle turned for the lorry for a second time. Trudging across the snow, she left Clare and Buzz to pirouette across the track. Up past the empty stands they went, the eerie quietness reminded Clare of home. The stands at Dunstall Park were always empty when they worked in the mornings. Something about the peace and quiet, of a place designed for noise and action, made Clare smile.

He had settled down now and the initial excitement of being out of his box in the fresh air had started to wear off. He stretched his neck down and sniffed at the snow as he walked, nearly kicking himself on the chin with every stride. After a few moments, with the stands a fair way behind them, Clare found herself following the rails around the 'P'. Deciding she may as well walk the whole course now, they turned the first right hand bend. Clare was focussed on the surface, the distance and the environment. Always thinking one step ahead of him, Clare tried to anticipate Buzz's thought processes. Could she spot anything that might cause him a problem, make him lose focus when running? Soaking up the feel of the track and having a good look at the immediate surroundings, she found herself at the second corner.

As James had warned her, the corner came up fast and veered off to the right to join the home straight. The surface here felt more slippery. She would need to watch for that when riding him here. She didn't want any accidents. If he slipped and fell, he would never trust the surface enough to run a winning race on it. This was the kind of surface that gave the snow shoes their chance to shine and boy did she hope they would shine!

Checking her watch, she discovered that they had been out for 40 minutes, a shade longer than she'd wanted but given her near miss with the skijoring pair, she thought herself lucky they weren't spending the afternoon chasing Buzz around the lake! Turning left back down the straight, in the direction of the barn, Clare could see more horses had started to warm up in the polo arena. One horse stood out from the rest. Zatoof stood nearly a whole hand higher than your average thoroughbred and his jet black coat carved him out like a silhouette against the white backdrop. Watching him striding powerfully across the snow, as though it was a grassy field, Clare knew he had the experience to give him the edge in the race, the race that was only two days away. What no one knew was, did he have the heart to win?

Leaving the track and crossing back into the lorry park, Clare could see their empty space as they passed it. She knew Michelle must have successfully started the lorry and gone for a drive. Tucking Buzz back into his box to watch the skiers on the slopes, Clare busied herself with skipping him out and making his lunch. By the time she'd topped up his water with electrolytes and flicked his coat over with a brush, Michelle had arrived back.

Stomachs growling, they headed for the town. Clare planned to ride Buzz mid-afternoon before the sun went down so they had a couple of hours to kill. Clare fancied trying the traditional Swiss fondue that James had raved about. Dipping chunks of bread into molten cheese of varying flavours was just what the girls needed! They found a small local restaurant that served the fondue and the girls ate their fill. The restaurant was empty except for the owner and the girls. Pictures of horses racing across the white turf adorned the walls. Some were black and white and some were colour shots, horses in skijoring races and horses playing polo. The equine athletes had been captured at their zenith; freeze framed and hung on the wall for the enjoyment of the customers.

Michelle had not found an equestrian shop on her drive, which meant Buzz was without a rug. As they discussed who to ask if there was a shop, or if anyone had any spares they could borrow, Clares' mind began to drift. Her eyes were glued to the walls, fascinated by the intensity of the photographs and the power of the horses portrayed within. The trust and faith those horses gave to their mounts overwhelmed Clare. They gave their all, not for a fee, sometimes not even for a kind word but because they wanted to. Did Buzz want to? Did he have what it took to have his portrait hung on the wall alongside the others? She had to find out. Paying the bill and tipping the owner well, they made their way back to the barn. Clare was going to work Buzz on the lake for the first time.

Having not ridden a horse for three days, Clare instantly felt at home when Michelle legged her up into the saddle. They were outside the barn but as one, they moved together towards the arena. It was quiet inside with a couple of other horses working in the far corner but Clare intended to keep clear and keep Buzz focussed. She would walk for 10 minutes and then trot. Depending on how well he handled that would determine whether she would take him out onto the track and try a working canter up the straight. Clare wanted a steady bit of work but nothing too fast and furious.

Having other ideas and bored of walking Buzz pushed himself into a trot. Not wanting to hold him back, Clare allowed him to go forward. He moved well enough, if a little careful in his movement to start with but the more he trotted, the less he thought about it and the more relaxed the pace became. Apprehensive, Clare fought her own emotions. She didn't want Buzz to pick up on her feelings and react adversely to them. Heading out towards the track, Buzz coiled under her like a spring. Although it was snow covered, Buzz knew a track when he saw one and the anticipation of the canter to come was almost too much for him. Cantering on the spot, he travelled sideways through the gap in the rails. Clare sat tall and quiet, stroking his neck and whispering down to him in low tones.

He shimmied across to the right rail, so tipping slightly forwards, shifting her balance Clare gave him the signal to go. Buzz surged forward and immediately started leaping about. With every stride, he cat leaped. Struggling to pull him up, Clare couldn't see any reason for it. He wasn't lame or stiff. He was wearing his usual tack and so far the surface hadn't seemed to cause him issue.

Michelle had been standing back by the bridge, could see what was happening and ran over to explain. As Buzz cantered, the movement of his front legs kicked snow up underneath him. The snow peppered his stomach and must have felt very strange. Unfamiliar with this sensation Michelle observed that Buzz had looked like he was trying to jump over and away from the flying snow. In an effort to teach him that this was not an issue and that the kick back wouldn't hurt him, Michelle gently threw some snow under his belly. Buzz leapt up in alarm with his eyes rolling and snorted in disgust at Michelle. At least they had figured out the problem, however Clare's only option was to ride him through it until he made the link himself. She knew Buzz was far better working things through in his own mind than being force fed. With that she turned him back towards the straight and kicked on. Away they went plunging and leaping through the snow. Buzz leapt left and right with every stride. Clare's main concern was keeping his head up. If he got his head down, then the plunging would turn into bucking and she didn't fancy ending up face first in the snow! Driving him on, she insisted he worked through it and gradually with each step, the plunges became smaller. He ploughed on in canter, throwing in the odd hop and skip but he was starting to work more smoothly. He started to grasp the concept, the snow caused no harm. It tickled and flicked onto the underside of his stomach and up the inside of his hind legs, but it didn't hurt. The further he went, the more desensitised he became and by the time they came into the second bend he had settled. His breathing regulated and his flow improved as each stride took him forward. Ears pricked, he started to enjoy it. Instead of concentrating on what was happening underneath him, he looked ahead. Clare was all too aware that this bend was slippery in places and was relieved he was concentrating better and not clowning around now. As the pace quickened, the snow shoes took effect. Biting into the snow, they held him firm as he cantered back left and onto the home straight.

Clare pulled him up next to Michelle for a short time, allowing him to recover keeping him walking in circles whilst she discussed the canter with Michelle.

"He seemed to settle to that OK. How did he look from here? It's a bit like teaching him to canter through water. The splashing and the sensation can unsettle some horses and it didn't occur to me that this would be the same. Night Flyer can't have had the same reaction otherwise James would have warned me." Out of breath from the negotiations she'd been having with Buzz, Clare spoke down to Michelle from Buzz's back.

"Yeah, he looked OK. He went off like a rodeo pony but by the time you got him back down that straight, he seemed to settle down. Are you going again?"

"Sure. I've only got today and tomorrow and that's it. He's got to get on with the job." She nodded then once again turned for the track. This time, he sprang straight into a good rhythm. Having found his confidence and still excited from the first canter, he pulled hard wanting more and more speed. Clare wanted to let him fly but knew that would have to wait for the morning. She wanted a strong canter this time but not a pipe opener. Buzz needed to save himself for race day. Her job was to show him the ropes, let him get the feel of the snow and give him the confidence to push himself to his limits on Sunday.

The pair loped around, steady and workman-like, they made good progress. Clare deliberately kept him to the left of where they had just been so that he ran on fresh snow and not the churned up snow that they had just cantered across. That way, he would avoid getting caught in a foot hole, possibly tripping and would still have fresh snow kicking up under his stomach familiarising him with the feeling. Pleased with the afternoon's work, Clare cooled him down back in the arena then hopped off and led him back to the barn.

Clare felt it had been a bit of an anti-climax. She had been so looking forward to working him on the snow. For weeks she had been thinking about how it would feel and what he would do on the surface, yet here she was leading him back to the barn. It had all been over in minutes flat. His plunging and leaping about had distracted her to start with and dealing with that issue meant she hadn't had time to enjoy the moment. She'd had visions of them both sailing across the snow together in a graceful and professional way; instead they had catapulted across the track like a pair of bucking broncos!

"Buzz, Buzz, Buzz!" sighing she chuckled. He was never straight forward and at every turn he threw in something new to keep her on her toes. That was why she loved him so; he made her think, kept her focussed and gave her a challenge. Riding Buzz made Clare feel alive and it was that feeling that made him so addictive for her.

The barn was busier now than it had been that morning and there were various grooms milling around attending to their horses. Zatoof's groom was hovering by his box when they arrived back. Introducing herself in excellent English, she shook Clare's hand.

"Nice English horse, Buzz. Does he like the snow?" Helena asked.

"He rode out OK, a bit fresh, but that's Buzz for you!" replied Clare, giving nothing away and a bit put out by the reference to Buzz's nationality.

"Zatoof loves the snow, don't you boy?" She proudly stroked his nose as he stood inspecting the activity in the barn over his box door.

"He won last year didn't he? He's a huge horse, almost too big for a racehorse!" Touché thought Clare as she struck back.

"He doesn't have to work as hard, each stride carries him further. It's a blessing he is so big." Helena explained as she fed him a treat from her palm. Zatoof hoovered it up and rolled it around in his mouth before crunching down on it hard. Helena walked over to Buzz's door. Greeting his visitor, Buzz stepped forward and sniffed her hand. Reaching back into her pocket she started to unwrap a boiled sweet.

"Can he have a bonbon?"

"No!" snapped Clare, alarmed at the suggestion. Feeding treats was unthinkable, a forbidden practice in most yards. Firstly, a horse can easily choke on a sweet. Secondly horses are not designed to eat human food and thirdly there are so many banned substances in racing, to prevent performance enhancing drugs being used to cheat, that to have a competitor's groom feed your horse was unacceptable! Totally off limits and Clare's tone made that crystal clear!

"Oh sorry! I didn't mean to offend you." Helena, realising her error, backed off. Putting the sweet back in her pocket, she retreated to Zatoof's stable and busied herself checking his rugs.

Clare was not in St. Moritz to make friends. She had a job to do and a horse to care for. Compromising herself and potentially the race would be professional suicide, so she made no effort to smooth over the situation. Buzz was off limits to anyone else, end of story!

Chapter 12

Ignoring the awkwardness that had arisen between Helena and herself, she concentrated on finishing off Buzz after his workout on the track. She brushed off the excess snow and thoroughly picked out his hooves, she cleared the snow that was impacted inside the shoe. Carefully avoiding the sensitive frog, she carved the "V" shape out and brushed the excess from his heel. It was then that she spotted it. A nasty quarter crack had developed on his nearside hind, on the hoof wall. It was on the left side and a good half way up. This was a serious problem. Buzz would surely be lame from it. Clare felt like she'd been punched as the gravity of the situation hit her. All the preparations, the travel and the hopes were surely dashed. Sitting on the straw bank looking blankly at Buzz and his broken hoof, Clare's mind was spinning. What on earth could she do? Call James or the vet? The vet seemed like a more productive option.

Across the car park and out into the dark she ran. The sun had dropped behind the mountains and like flicking a light switch it was dark. Clare ran as fast as her legs would carry her to the veterinary offices. Desperately she burst through the door.

"Please come. My horse, Buzz needs a vet!"

"OK. I come now" replied a voice. It came from a small dark haired woman sitting at a desk completing paperwork. She had answered Clare without looking up but then continued writing.

"No. You don't understand. You must come now. He has a quarter crack. It's urgent!"

"I do understand and I am coming now!" Annoyed, the woman rose

---

from her seat and sauntered over to collect her coat and bag. She obviously wasn't overly enthusiastic about the prospect. Every second was painful and agonising as Clare waited for her to get her coat and gloves on and locate the keys to lock the office.

On the way to the barn, Clare explained what work he had done that day and that he didn't seem lame or sore. She was sure he was fine after the journey and the vet who had checked him that very morning hadn't spotted a crack in his hoof. Babbling with nervousness, the vet simply nodded and listened, knowing nothing she could offer at this point would make the slightest bit of difference.

Inside his box Buzz, seemed unfazed. However, when Clare led him from the box his discomfort was clear. Removing his shoes and inspecting the hoof, the vet offered no more than, "I don't think he will run." She then prattled on about the freezing temperatures combined with the brittle nature of thoroughbred hooves. Clare didn't hear anything after, "I don't think he will run." Her head was swimming. Wanting to cry, she tried to contain her feelings. Walking and hopping Buzz back into his box, Clare thanked the vet and turned back to Buzz. Alone again with him, she sobbed. The frustration poured from her, as the tears ran down her cheeks and onto his neck. Buzz, sensing her turmoil, stood quietly and patiently, allowing her to hold him whilst her heart quietly broke. Clare felt totally alone. She was miles from home, in a strange place, with a horse that couldn't run.

Michelle, still blissfully unaware of the drama, arrived in the barn. Seeing Clare's red eyes she realised there was a problem.

"What's happened? Is he OK?"

"Oh Michelle! He's got a quarter crack! A bloody big one! Vet's been and reckons he won't run…"

Clare's words hung in the air while Michelle processed the news.

"What do you mean, a quarter crack? He was fine on the track. Let me see." Michelle entered the box, confused that the horse she had seen less than two hours ago, cavorting around on the track was now lame and unable to run. Looking at the hoof she saw the crack and her shoulders slumped. "Shit, you'd better ring James. Oh this is bad news! I brought your phone down here. It's charged now." Taking the phone, Clare left the box and walked out of the barn to make the call.

Taking a deep breath, she dialled James. Dreading what she was about to say, she put the mobile to her ear.

"Hello? Clare, how's it going?" He sounded happy and excited.

"Listen James, we have a problem. He has a quarter crack! I'm sorry James. The vet says he isn't going to run."

Silence was the response and then;

"Bullshit! It must be a fresh crack. I can't talk now but do nothing. I'm on the vintage train from Chur and I'll be there in 45 minutes tops." In complete denial and refusing to accept that Buzz wouldn't run, he slammed down the phone. Clare knew he wouldn't let on to Alistair and Miranda but keep stum, until he saw the horse himself. Either way, the old adage, "No foot, no horse," was the thought rattling through both of their minds.

****

"You guys settle into your room and I will be back later with Clare for drinks, after I've seen her and Buzz." James dropped Alistair and Miranda at their hotel, The Kulm, along with the bus load of luggage they had brought for the three day trip. Preoccupied by the news from Clare, he couldn't wait to get away from them and get to the barn. When she had called to give him the news, they had all been on board the vintage train that was laboriously chugging through the Alps towards St. Moritz. The plume of steam and the painted iron engine, together with the old wooden carriages set against the wintery back drop, made it look like a scene from Dr Zhivago. James, Alistair and Miranda were enjoying this part of the trip more than any other and the nearer they got to St. Moritz, the jollier the vibe between the three became.

Having enjoyed a bottle or two of wine on the train, James was into his stride telling tales of his last visit here with Night Flyer. Enthralled by James' vivid recounts, they had all been jolted into reality when James' phone rang. James decided not to tell Alistair and Miranda at this point. It would be pointless. Until he had seen the horse and spoken with the vet, no decisions could be made. Not wanting Miranda's hysteria adding to the stress, he tried his best to hide his concern over Buzz. However, Alistair and Miranda had the distinct impression that something about the call had aggravated him. Not wanting to pry, in case it was a personal matter between him and Clare, it wasn't mentioned but the general tone had changed and they were just as pleased to be leaving him at the hotel entrance as he was to be leaving them. Telling the taxi driver where he wanted to be dropped off James, sank into the back of the cab, steeling himself for what he was about to find.

Sitting outside Buzz's box, Clare waited for James. The mood in the barn was of silent apprehension. She had no idea how James would react once he saw the crack and so emotionally drained by the events of the last few days, she couldn't rationally think of a resolution. Clare was used to being in control, dealing with situations and solving issues with her horses. However this time she felt vulnerable, like a fish out of water she was flapping. The language barrier and alien environment made her feel alone and helpless. All she could do was sit and wait for James and hopefully he would come up with a solution.

Michelle had wisely retired back to the hotel, predicting that James' frustration would turn to fury and she didn't fancy getting caught in the crossfire. She knew Clare well enough to know, that under these circumstances, what Clare needed was peace and quiet and thinking time. Michelle had planned on trying to enjoy what could well turn out to be her last night in St. Moritz. She knew there was nothing she could do for Clare, James or Buzz. The stark reality was that they had travelled across Europe with Buzz, the only English horse in the race and for his chance to be snatched from him like this now was gut wrenching.

Marching into the barn, James was ready for action. Looking up, Clare could see he was fired up. Fuelled by a lifetime of wanting, he wasn't going to let this one drop.

"Come on, get him out then. Let's see the damage," he said. No time for niceties.

Clare didn't have the energy to pick a fight over his tone, so instead, up she got to get Buzz from his box and led him into the centre of the barn, standing him straight for James to inspect him. Buzz wasn't in a huge amount of pain but he was visibly lame. He was bored by the repeated disturbance and kicked out in annoyance.

"Still up to his old tricks then. He can't be that bad!" James muttered as he bent down to see the hoof. "Bloody marvellous!" was the response once he had seen the crack. "When did this happen?"

"On exercise, this afternoon. He was absolutely fine. Sound and he cantered OK. I saw it when I came back in to dress him over."

"Which vet looked at it?" asked James accusingly.

"The resident vet. They're in the office. I went straight over and asked her to come and look at him."

"OK, and she said he won't run, is that right?"

"Yes, that's what she said." The words stuck in her throat as she said them. The crushing disappointment weighed heavily on her and she was desperately trying to hold it together.

Bored with standing still, Buzz decided he was off to inspect the barn and lunging forward, he caught Clare off guard and they took a few steps along the barn with Clare groping at the lead rope before she got him back under control again.

"Well, he walked well enough then!" James remarked. "I'm getting a second opinion. We haven't come this far to bail out now. Look, the way I see it, is that if he were on three legs there would be no chance but he is weight bearing well enough. There might be a chance so we've got to try. I'm going to call Christian and see if there is another vet that will come and see him."

Resigned to the fact that he wouldn't run, Clare nodded in agreement. She felt James needed to work it through in his own mind and come to the same conclusion everyone else had. If it took another vet to tell him that Buzz wouldn't run, then so be it. James headed back out of the barn in the same determined manner he had marched in and Clare put Buzz back in his box. She then returned to the straw bale outside the box to wait for the next part of the evening to take shape.

It wasn't long before James returned, with Christian and another guy who Clare guessed was a vet, the kit bag a bit of a tell-tale sign. Without being asked, she once again led Buzz into the barn. Talking between themselves and inspecting his hoof, they ignored Clare as she stood quietly stroking Buzz's head, whispering into his ear as she did so. He was sleepy. It had been a long day, filled with new sights, sounds and sensations and he stood resting his hind leg, with his ears at half-mast. Listening to her voice, it lulled him off to sleep.

Fiddling in his bag, the vet produced a bottle of alcohol. Deciding he needed to clean the crack thoroughly and ascertain the depth, he poured it onto Buzz's foot. It stung a bit and Buzz jerked his head up, startled by the sensation. Clare and James looked on in horror as the

alcohol seeped into the crack peeling the hoof wall back as it did so, opening the crack further! The vet seemed indifferent and asked for some tape.

"It's in the lorry," said Clare, unable to drag her eyes away from Buzz's hoof.

James returned with the tape. Similar to duct-tape, it was tough and fibrous on the inside and waterproof on the outside creating a barrier. The vet swiftly and expertly bound Buzz's hoof, tighter and tighter he wrapped the entire hoof in tape. The support the tape gave should keep the hoof intact and give Buzz the confidence to walk without pain or further damage.

"I have treated many horses like this. It's the snow and the cold that makes the hooves crack. Work him tomorrow and see how he goes. Compared to some it's not that deep. He could be OK, although I can't promise. Depends how tough he is," instructed the vet, as he packed his bag ready to leave. "I will return tomorrow lunchtime to see him again." Shaking hands with James and Christian he left.

"Swiss show jumping vet apparently," said James. "He knows his stuff."

"Ummm hopefully," was all Clare could muster, not daring to let herself believe for one minute that Buzz was still in with a chance. She was shattered. Drained by yet another emotionally, gruelling day.

"Look you'll ride him in the morning and make a decision then. He could do it Clare. You know how tough he is and like the vet said, it's only a small crack, not that deep." Reassured by the vet's advice James was like a dog with a bone. She knew he wouldn't let it go unless he absolutely had to.

"Yes, I'll ride him tomorrow and yes he might be OK. We'll have to see." Closing the stable door behind her, they turned for the barn doors. Her work that day with Buzz was done. All they could do now was try to get some rest and see what tomorrow would bring.

During the drama of the evening, James had received a call from Dean Wellings. He too had arrived in St. Moritz and wanted to meet for a drink. Travelling with his friend Darren, the IRB had arranged accommodation just along from Alistair and Miranda at the Hotel Soldanella. Despite the question mark hanging over Buzz's run, James wanted to go out that evening. He needed to wine and dine Alistair and Miranda: Michelle had her glad rags on and was ready and raring to go and Dean and Darren were set to paint the town red. The only one who couldn't bear the thought of idle chit chat and pleasantries was Clare. All she wanted to do, was crawl back to her grubby hotel room and hide until the morning.

****

Through an admin error, James was booked to stay at the same hotel as Alistair and Miranda so he headed off to spruce himself up for the evening. He planned to eat in the hotel with Clare, Michelle, Alistair and Miranda then meet up with Dean and Darren at a local bar he wanted to revisit. Leaving Clare to wash and change, he could see she wasn't in the mood for a night out.

"Come on, it's all part of the game. If we don't go they'll realise there is a serious problem. I'm going to tell them but I'm going to play it down. No point spooking everyone now. Poor Dean will cry like a baby if he thinks his chance to run on Sunday has gone. And as for Alistair and Miranda, well do I need to spell it out? Have a shower and get changed. Sulking up here isn't going to change anything," James said encouragingly.

Grudgingly Clare agreed. Besides she was hungry and a good feed would set her up well for what would inevitably be a long day tomorrow. She was looking forward to seeing Dean too. Feeling she had an ally in him, she knew he understood Buzz; that he had felt his power and appreciated him which was a comforting thought.

An hour later and they were all sitting around an oval table in James' hotel. The five of them had ordered and the topic of conversation was of course Buzz.

"The vet has seen him and wrapped his foot. He'll be fine I'm sure. I've seen much worse," bluffed James.

"Yes, but will it affect his run? I mean we haven't come all this way for a placing James, we want a win." Alistair indignantly reminded James of the costs incurred by this trip, making it very clear that anything less than first place simply would not do.

"He'll give it his best shot Alistair. Of that I'm sure," James replied, glancing over at Clare and Michelle who were doing nothing to confirm or deny the position. "More wine Miranda?" James switched subjects. "Skiing, let me ask about your skiing. Are you ready for the slopes tomorrow?"

"Ooh, I can't wait," she said like an over excited puppy. "I've booked myself and Alistair for an afternoon's skiing on the nursery slopes so Alistair can get a feel for it. I'm much more advanced than him so we need to take it slowly," she explained arrogantly. She was wearing a beige trouser suit; well fitted on her sleek figure and not a hair out of place. A diamond bracelet glinted on her fake tanned wrist and Clare wondered if the cost of her beauty treatment was included in Alistair's budget for the trip. Clare felt underdressed. She hadn't bothered packing much in the way of dining clothes. She had a pair of brown trousers and a nice woollen jumper on with her glorious auburn hair woven neatly into a braid. Instead of diamonds on her wrist she wore a small silver bangle bought by her mother for her 21st birthday. Unaware of her natural beauty and the fact that most men in the restaurant had turned to look as she had arrived, Clare sat wondering what it was like to have the time and money to pamper one's self like Miranda. Despite all her efforts to appear classy and sophisticated, she always managed to overdo it. The end result being a poor imitation, cheap and fake looking. Her silicone enhanced breasts and poker straight hair somehow made her look too prepared and Clare decided she'd rather settle for a pair of wellies and woolly socks any day!

As the meal wore on, Clare started to feel sleepier and sleepier. The hearty meal and the warm restaurant were adding to her lethargy as she struggled to show interest in the conversation. The rest of the party were tucking into their third bottle of wine and arranging to have the meal put on their tab before heading off to join Dean and Darren. By this time, all Clare wanted to do was sleep! James went out to reception to order a taxi to take them all to the bar and Clare took the chance to exit stage left.

"Thanks guys for a lovely evening. It's great to be here with you all but I'm going to head off now. I've an early start with Buzz and I need to be fresh for it." She went over and kissed Alistair and Miranda in the continental two cheek fashion. Following James out to reception, she found him on his mobile to Dean arranging a meeting point. Slightly disappointed that she wouldn't see Dean, she tapped James' shoulder.

"I'm off James. I can't be doing with drinking tonight. I need to get my head down so you go and enjoy yourself and I'll see you in the barn tomorrow morning." Pecking him on the cheek, she wrapped her coat around her shoulders and headed back out into the cold for her chalet.

****

Saturday 22nd February

Today, the horses running in the Grosser Preis, would parade in the arena for their owners, trainers and the officials from the White Turf and the IRB. It was a yearly ritual and one that Buzz had to take part in. Clare wanted to get back to him early that morning to see how his hoof had held up overnight and prepare him for the parade. In the afternoon there were to be three flat races followed by three skijoring races run on the track and Clare was keen to see for herself how the place worked on a race day.

Dean Wellings had travelled out to St. Moritz to ride Buzz on the track at least once before the race. He had never experienced the feel of the snow and was looking forward to being back on Buzz. Having enjoyed his previous rides, he had been daydreaming about Buzz, strong and powerful under him as they flew together across the frozen lake. Dean had enough experience to know what a quarter crack was and knew James was bluffing when he said, "it wasn't that bad." Keen to see for himself, he too planned to get to the barn early, catch up with Clare and find out exactly what the state of play was.

Finding her mucking out Buzz's box, he was relieved to see Buzz tucking into his breakfast and that the hoof remained well taped. Buzz was standing evenly on all four hooves clearly indicating that he didn't feel too sore on the hoof.

"Morning Clare. Good to see you. Sorry I missed you last night," he said.

"Oh hi Dean. Blimey you're down here early! Yeah sorry. I was so tired last night I had to get my head down. What with this bugger and his hoof, I couldn't think straight. You OK? How was your journey?"

"Good thanks, and last night was a laugh. That Miranda's a handful when she's had a few!" he said raising his eyebrows and giving a knowing nod.

"Quite a filly isn't she?" laughed Clare.

"How's the boy then? Hoof OK?"

"This morning, so far so good! He's weight bearing so I just need

to get him out and trot him up."

"I'll give you a hand once he's had his breakfast if you like. I might as well make myself useful now I'm here."

"Sure, no worries. Go and grab a coffee while I finish up and then we can get him out and see. Don't suppose you've seen James anywhere this morning have you?"

"Nope. It was 3am when we left so he'll still be in his pit!"

"Oi Wellings! Don't sell me short! I heard that!" James shouted light heartedly as he arrived. "It might have been 3am but I'm up and here to see to the horse so don't you worry!"

James looked a little dishevelled but none the less, in true Unett fashion, he fully intended to get the day underway.

"Let's get him out then and see how he looks."

It was clear to all three that Buzz wasn't feeling lame. Bursting through his stable door, eager to be outside again, he dragged Clare towards the barn doors.

"Alright, alright, steady lad. Settle down." She repeated the mantra over and over.

"Looks alright from here," said James. "What do you think Dean?"

"Yep, looks right as rain."

"Well, we'll get him on the arena and see how he holds up. That alright with you Jonesy?"

"Yes sir!" Clare nodded back with an air of mockery. She could feel that Buzz felt well. Keen to walk out and happy to weight bear and turn, for a second she thought perhaps he could run after all? Reigning in her optimism, as a means of self-preservation, she knew they weren't out of the woods yet. He still had to work in the arena and have a second vet check, although, so far so good.

The arena was getting busy. Hanging over the rails were owners, trainers and officials, all keen to see the listed race contenders strut their stuff. Being a race day, the whole complex was busier. Stalls were being dragged out onto the track, horses were arriving and staff and stewards were everywhere.

She intended to get Buzz out there and warmed up; allow him to burn off some steam but at the same time keep him contained. Preserving his hoof to the best of her ability was her priority. If there was any chance he could run tomorrow, he needed to be fit and able as he could be.

There were already five runners working in the arena when Clare burst in. Buzz did not like the idea of any kind of containment. He thought it was race day and was fired up and ready to go. No sign of lameness. The quarter crack not even registering in his mind. He wanted to race that much was clear. The onlookers stood by the rails, stunned as the 'English horse' and his tiny jockey cartwheeled around the arena.

Heartened by his typical 'Buzz-like' behaviour, Alistair and Miranda were busy making it known to anyone who would listen, that he was their horse. Sashaying around in a full body ski suit, complete with furry hat, she looked like a lollipop. When Clare and Buzz passed her by, he shied violently away from her and her shockingly vivid outfit. Clare chuckled to herself as perched on his back, perfectly balanced and moving in harmony with him, he twisted and kicked his way across the snow. His movement felt even and balanced. Maybe he could do it after all! The longer he worked, the more confident she felt and when he trotted along soundly, she couldn't help but grin. Her Buzz. Her boy. To her he was awesome. He so loved his racing, and was going to tough it out and get on with his job, despite his hoof. Cantering came just as easily to him and he sprang across the surface, collected and coiled, ready to perform.

The session came to an end and James met her at the rails with the vet.

"I don't think we need to fiddle with his foot. He looks good to me. I'm going to pass him clear to run tomorrow. No exercise now until the race. Don't push your luck!" said the vet.

"Thanks. But, no exercise? He's only been out there once! The jockey needs a spin on him too, surely?" James questioned, relieved but exasperated.

"Look, if you want that hoof to hold for tomorrow, you will have to rest him for the remainder of the day. If you don't, you risk making it worse and not running him at all," retorted the vet sternly.

"OK, OK, take him in Clare. I'll find Dean and tell him the good news! Thanks again Doc." Bidding him farewell, James stalked off in hot pursuit of Dean and Darren, last seen sloping off to the bar.

Clare and Buzz jogged over to the car park. She was so overwhelmed by the news she was dumbstruck! He would run! HE WOULD RUN! Leaping off outside the barn, she led him back inside

to untack him. The one sided conversation would have seemed funny to anyone else but to the two of them it was the norm. Explaining the whole situation, as if he could understand every word, she fussed around him, brushing and stroking him as she went. He stood a little bemused; he had planned on running a race right there and then. What he didn't realise was that he would get his chance, the very next day!

Chapter 13

The tented village had turned from an eerily quiet and deserted venue into a hive of activity. The atmosphere was jubilant as the crowds gathered to watch the afternoons' racing. St. Moritz has hosted the European Snow Meet annually since 1907 and their experience showed. The tented village provided for all types of punter; from the rich and famous, to the run of the mill race goer. There were coffee tents, bars, live music and sponsorship tents for the likes of BMW and Orange. People flooded the walkways and tents alike as the afternoon sun shone down on them.

There was a mixture of skijoring and flat races scheduled for that afternoon and the bookmakers were in full flow as James wandered through the centre of the village in search of Dean. Passing through the stands, he made his way to the bar next to the jockeys' tent. An educated guess told him he would find Dean and Darren in there and he wasn't wrong.

"Dean!" James shouted over the music and chatter. "Dean. Over here!"

Looking round, Dean spotted James, and grabbing his beer bottle, he squeezed through the wall of people still waiting to be served.

"Hi! Do you want a drink mate?" Dean asked. "Darren's getting another round in. It's mobbed in here! Plenty of totty too," said Dean cheekily, with a school boy glint in his eye.

"Yeah, bottle of Peroni please," James shouted over to Darren at the bar. "Anyway, never mind about the totty, you've got a job to do tomorrow and I want your full attention. There's plenty of time for chasing skirt after you win! Besides, they are not going to be interested in a skinny little bit like you. Look at all the strapping German blokes. You've got some stiff competition there!" laughed James.

It was true enough though, both James and Dean looked pint sized in comparison to the rest of the male talent in the bar. They were all huge, broad and tall to boot.

"Job to do James? Did you just say a job to do? Is he running then?" Dean asked in disbelief.

"Yes, the old rogue is running! He'll be grand but you won't be able to work him beforehand. He's done all he can do on the track until the race. Before you pipe up I know it's not ideal, but we've no choice. Vet's orders."

With that, Darren appeared with the drinks. Slurping down his beer, Dean looked like he needed it to steady himself after James' news.

"Bloody hell James! I've never worked a horse on stuff like this before. Christ you don't just want a ride either, you want a bloody win! You sure about all this? I mean it's not exactly odds on for us is it?" Dean was right. Both he and Buzz were novices on the ice. Buzz had never galloped on it and Dean had never ridden on it! Buzz had a quarter crack and the hot favourite was looking very strong.

"I couldn't give a shit about the bloody odds. I broke my back at your age. What were the odds of me riding again….? Not very bloody high but here we are. So stop your whinging and get on with it Dean. The horse is good enough and could run it backwards, all you have to do is let him. I have wanted this for years and this is my chance, Buzz's chance, so drink up man!" Lifting his bottle, they chinked the tops together in unison and drank their fill.

Clare had left Buzz to rest for the afternoon. She wanted to catch up with Michelle; they had spotted a little seating area with sun loungers that overlooked the lake and she fancied a hot chocolate and a good sit down before the afternoons' racing began. Leaving the barn to make her way back to the chalet, Clare could hear the roar of the distant crowd from the tented village. The noise generated by the mass of people congregating together echoed around the mountains. The relief she felt at Buzz's vetting result would be short lived. Worries over his lack of experience on the track and his hoof holding up had started to set in. Banishing the negative thoughts from her mind, she walked back into her room to find Michelle listening to Robbie

Williams at full pelt again!

"Michelle, he's going to run!" Clare blurted out the good news like an excited child. "The vet says that we can't run him on the ice again though until the race but that he can run!"

"Yesssss," said Michelle punching the air. "I just wanna feeeeeel real love in the home that I live in!"

Clare flopped down on the bed next to her laughing at her silliness.

"I didn't think he'd pass him. I thought we'd come all this way for nothing. I can't believe it!" confessed Clare. "James' face was a picture. This means so much to him. I would hate to think what would happen if he hadn't been allowed to run. Let's hope he runs well. I mean, I know he has limited experience but he should be OK. That Zatoof looks like he could run round the track five times before breaking a sweat though!"

"I know and Helena is really scary looking. Have you seen her arms? They're massive! I bet she could carry you round five times with him!"

"I've got to get out into the sunshine. D'you fancy grabbing a hot chocolate and chilling out for half an hour at that place down the road, before we go over to the tented village?"

"Sure. It'd be good to get out of here. What time's the first race?" asked Michelle as she got up from the bed and sauntered over to the dressing table to brush her hair.

"About 2ish I think. It's the skijoring race first. I've got to see that. They must be nuts!" said Clare.

"Come on then, we'd better hurry it up a bit. It's 12.30 now and I fancy placing a bet! Oh and don't forget your €40 bet on Buzz for the dude at the check point. We have to place that one for him!" Michelle reminded Clare.

Laying out on loungers in the Swiss sunshine the girls looked like a couple of teenagers on a school ski trip. Supping on their frothy hot chocolates, they clenched their mugs through fingerless gloves. Clare was wearing her boots, jeans and a red ski jacket. Her hair pulled into a pony tail that poked through the hole in the back of her denim baseball cap. Michelle had opted for a more traditional look and had dressed in a matching coat and trouser set in baby blue and pale yellow. Her mousey brown hair was pushed back behind her sun glasses that were shoved into her hair line to keep it out of her eyes. They could

hear the commotion across the lake building and some of the afternoon's racehorses were warming up in the arena. Others were being tacked up into skijoring harness before their drivers backed them into the ski mounted carts in readiness for the action.

Michelle had a race day schedule and they sat reading the names of the horses and trainers, weighing up their selection before placing their bets. Clare wasn't a keen gambler, preferring the relationship with the horse to the relationship with her finances she rarely betted. Today though, she wanted to bet on a skijoring horse called 'Norton's Legende.' He was a stocky, dapple grey trotter gelding she'd seen at the far end of the barn. He was quite a character. His groom had complained about the way he kept tipping his water bucket over and how he then picked it up with his teeth and threw it over the stable door. His bed had been soaked through three times yesterday and the groom had spent most of the day shovelling wet bedding into a barrow. Norton's Legende had looked on, almost smiling, at what he thought was a great joke! He had learned that tipping his bucket got him attention. Clearly a people horse, he enjoyed the company of his groom who had barely managed 10 minutes to herself all day! Clare liked a horse with character and she fancied he was quite good at his job. The quirky ones always were! Clare's phone rang; it was James wanting to know where she had got to. Arranging to meet him by the American Express tent, the girls headed over to the tented village in high spirits.

****

Placing her bet with moments to spare, Clare scrambled along the stands to where everyone was seated. The 'Grand Prix BMW Snow Trotting Challenge' was about to start. The skijoring horses were behind a line with their ski carts attached, the drivers 'holding their horses' as they stamped and snorted ready for action. The race covered the same distance as Buzz's race, 1900 metres or approximately 1 mile. However these horses would trot in the carts instead of galloping like the flat racers would. The bell rang and they were off. The drivers veered across the track vying to get into the best positions and the snow flew everywhere. They came hammering down the straight, heads high and legs flailing up and down like pistons in the snow. Norton's Legende was sitting third in from the rail, his driver's green silks billowing out behind them as they flew along. Around the first bend they went, the relentless trotting quite alien to most horse owners: when horses reached those kinds of speeds, they would normally break into a canter. These horses however, trotters, were bred for the knee action and gait that enabled them to trot efficiently and quickly. Norton's Legende looked like he was flagging along the back straight but as they turned into the second bend, things changed. The lead horse, a dark bay, broke into a canter which meant elimination for him. The second horse seemed to be going well but then his cart slid out to the right as they rounded the final part of the second bend where it joined the straight. The crowd let out a collective gasp as the cart swung towards Norton's Legende. Perhaps sensing danger or perhaps he could just see the finishing line, Norton's Legende dug in and extended. The ground covering pace quickened and he lengthened his body, almost streamlining himself as he stretched low and lithe towards the finish line. Winning by a skijoring length (horse and cart combined), he had won a fabulous race and his driver was standing in the cart punching the air in delight. The stocky grey gelding almost blended into the snowy background as he slowed down and turned around to come back into the winners' enclosure. A worthy win for the little horse with the big character! The crowd were fired up and the cheer they let rip when he came jogging back past the stands was deafening!

Clare watched his groom greet him at the gateway. She could see the tears of pride in her eyes as she led him off the track, the day of mucking out long forgotten. Clare wondered if that would be her tomorrow. She was snapped out of her day dream as Michelle nudged her.

"Come on. Let's get your winnings Jonesy!"

"Winnings!" said James shocked. "You had a bet?"

"Only a little one, because he was funny in the barn, kept throwing his water bucket out the box!" She told them the entire story and had them all laughing at the little grey's cheekiness.

Deciding to bet on the remaining races as a team, they all stuck €10 in the pot and took turns in choosing which horse to back. At the end of the last race they all got €14 back. Not the best return but they had all enjoyed the afternoon; the weather was kind and the racing good fun, especially the spectacle of the skijoring. It was exactly what was

needed after the stressful week they had all been through. Once again making her excuses, Clare felt the invisible umbilical cord between her and Buzz tugging. She needed to get back to him for evening stables.

They had all been invited to the IRB dinner at the five star, Survetta House Hotel that evening. Being the only British trainers at the meet, they were quite the celebrities. Clare, James, Alistair and Miranda had received invitations but sadly, Michelle, Dean and Darren had not. There were rumours that Lester Piggott was attending and Miranda was counting down the minutes until she would meet with the gentry of the racing world. She had just the outfit and with her matching Gucci bag and shoes, she was sure she'd wow them all.

Michelle, Dean and Darren were laughing about their lack of invitations and had arranged to meet up with the others after the meal, back at their hotel bar.

Buzz was snoozing when Clare returned to the barn. It had been busy with all the comings and goings of the racers that day and the jostling in the arena that afternoon had kept Buzz and his nosey attitude well occupied. He hadn't had a moments rest since Clare had left him and he was pooped! She checked his hoof, there was no change and he was happily standing on it. Skipping him out and feeding him, she could feel the nerves bubbling up again. Suppressing the butterflies, she kissed Buzz's nose.

"Goodnight lad. You get some rest. We've got our big day tomorrow!"

She left him nosing through his haylage, content and blissfully unaware of the day to follow.

****

Beep, Beep! The taxi sounded its horn outside the chalet. Clare leaned out the window acknowledging to James, Alistair and Miranda below, that she was on her way down. In a full length, black gown with a high, lacy neck which elegantly draped her lithe, toned body, Clare slipped gracefully into the taxi.

"You look lovely," said Miranda through gritted teeth.

"You certainly do," said Alistair genuinely.

Smiling quietly to himself, James said nothing. He didn't need to.

He had brought the outfit with him. Knowing Clare wouldn't have brought anything herself, and that Miranda would be kitted out to the hilt, he hadn't wanted Clare panicking over an outfit at the last minute. Taking advice from Clare's mum, he had purchased the dress and a shrug from a local dressmaker. After all, this was a once in a lifetime dinner and she should have a once in a lifetime dress.

Both he and Alistair were in dinner suits; clean shaven and sporting impossibly shiny shoes. Miranda was dressed in a burgundy gown, an off the shoulder number with a plunging neck line. Her hair was swept severely back from her face. Heavy eye make-up and far too much perfume completed the look.

"Thank you, so do you," replied Clare politely, choking on the perfume as she spoke! Blushing, she actually felt uncomfortable in her dress. Unlike Miranda, she was unused to glamour and grandeur. Clare felt out of her depth heading for the high society company she knew she would be mixing with that evening. Dreading putting her foot in it and getting the etiquette wrong, she was desperate to blend in and accompany James quietly and appropriately throughout the evening. Miranda was welcome to all the limelight and attention. As for Clare, she would rather have been sharing steak and chips in the pub!

The Survetta Hotel was set high above the town. It was a huge place with grand verandas overlooking the valley. It was suitably impressive as a venue in which to host such a dinner. Drawing into the driveway, they could see the palatial building, all eight storeys including a roof terrace, towered above them. Turrets with green copper roofs loomed either side of the entranceway.

The four were escorted by uniformed porters: from the car, up the stone steps covered in red carpet and through the glass doors into the foyer. Oak panelled walls gave it a regal feel. The place was clearly steeped in history. Hanging on the walls were black and white photographs depicting the hotel's history. It had been built in 1912 and managed by the Survetta family for six proud generations. Miranda had slipped off to reapply her lipstick so James and Clare took the opportunity to wander around soaking up the ambiance. Studying the photographs and admiring the craftsmanship that had gone into building such an incredibly impressive and successful hotel, it was the first time in days that they had been alone together for just a few moments. James wrapped his arm around her waist, pulling her nearer.

"You look pretty good Jonesy."

"You scrub up alright yourself Mr Unett," she smiled. Her pale skin and freckles gave her a girlish look. "Will he be OK tomorrow?" Feeling vulnerable, she needed some reassurance.

"If he wants to be. You know what he's like. It's up to him now," James replied truthfully. A little wounded, that despite the dress and a bucket load of compliments, all she was still thinking about was Buzz.

Nodding in agreement, they went back to picture gazing until all four were called through to the lounge. Staff from the IRB were greeting the guests and James was being introduced as, "James Unett, you know. The English trainer".

"I doubt they will introduce Lester as, "Lester Piggott, you know. The English jockey!" remarked James to Alistair as they strolled through the long thin room in search of a seat. Miranda had started name dropping and talking in the overly loud tone she acquired when she wanted to be over heard. Clare cringed at the sound of her voice as she spouted on about the school she had attended and the cost of her education.

Standing with Frau Mader, Zatoof's trainer, and Christian who had Double Fun entered for the Grosser von Preis, James was enjoying the banter. Clare sidled over, wanting to glean any snippets of information she could that would help her and Buzz tomorrow. Noticing Lester Piggott arrive, Clare wanted to be as far away from Miranda as possible. She would have bet on Miranda flouncing over and simpering over the famous jockey in the most unbearable way. As Clare slipped off to the toilets to avoid embarrassment, she heard the fatal words.

"Lester darling! So lovely to meet you. I'm Miranda Cavendish, Bressbee's owner."

Quickening her step, Clare fled to the sanctuary of the ladies. There, she shut herself in a booth and sat down on the closed lid. Tonight was going to be a nightmare! Miranda would get drunk and behave inappropriately. Alistair would say nothing of any worth to anyone, quietly drinking until he had the sense to remove Miranda out of further harm's way. James would flit between groups of people laughing and joking as he went, complimenting the women and rubbing shoulders with people of note. He would be 'working' this evening. Clare would hang around, make polite conversation and play her part as James' partner like the good girl she was. Worrying now that she would miss the call for dinner, she made her way back to the lounge.

Just in time, they were directed to take their places in the dining room. The cavernous room seemed endless and the horseshoe shaped table in the middle of the room looked like it could seat a thousand people! It was decorated with crystal glasses and polished cutlery and the napkins were folded to perfection. Ruby coloured velvet curtains dressed the floor to ceiling windows and at the end of the room was the biggest fireplace Clare had ever seen. More like a bonfire in proportions, the fire warmed the room giving it a welcoming, rustic feel. Gazing into the fire, she watched the flicker and crackle of the amber and golden flames, twisting and licking around the burning logs. The colours and energy of the fire reminded her of Buzz. Her beautiful dancing Buzz, never far from her mind. Escorted to their seats, Clare was relieved to discover that the owners were seated at one end and the trainers at the other. The IRB and special guests took the top table looking out towards the guests.

The banquet began and the wine flowed. Fish to start with, followed by a choice of beef or chicken for the main course and an array of fresh desserts to finish, were offered to the guests. Enjoying the delicious food, Clare chatted with Christian seated on her left while James was seated on her right. They laughed at Miranda, across the room, as she got louder and louder.

The guests, predominantly German, chatted easily and freely amongst themselves. Some were clearly known to each other, old friends or rivals perhaps and the evening's tone was relaxed. Clare was relieved that there wasn't too much pomp and ceremony; she had even managed to work out in what order she should use her cutlery! Waitresses lined the walls, ready to leap forth and refill wine glasses as soon as the level dropped below half. Even James had backed off, not wanting to get roaring drunk in front of some of the industry's greats he had tempered his intake. Clare opted for soft drinks; a fuzzy head the next morning wouldn't help the cause. Someone needed a clear head!

Miranda showed no such restraint. It was nearly 10pm and she was hooting and cackling like a witch. Alistair was starting to look uncomfortable, aware of the rising volume of her voice, he attempted to settle her down by placing his arm on hers. It did not go down well.

Loudly, she chastised him for spoiling her fun. Just as her rant was about to reach fever pitch, the toast master rang his bell.

The guests' attention was drawn from Miranda's tantrum to the top table, where Barbara Keller, the head of the IRB, gave a speech. She highlighted the importance of international racing and the support shown to foreign race meets. Thanking the guests for their continued support, she handed over to Lester. He started by complimenting the trainers, on getting through the ballot for the Grosser Preis, understanding himself how much work and dedication it took to get a horse into that favourable position. Moving on, to the admiration he had for both the horses and jockeys who would run on the ice, he asked the guests to raise their glasses to wish them safe passage during the race the following day. Much to James' pleasure, he also acknowledged their presence, saying he of course would be rooting for Buzz, the only British trained horse in the race! Tipping his glass to Lester, James smiled a grateful and proud smile.

What an achievement! James was thrilled. Clare knew he'd never ever speak of it in those terms. He was such a proud man and would never stoop to self-praise. She could however, almost feel him swell with pride. Genuinely chuffed for him, she squeezed his hand under the table and he squeezed back, grinning broadly.

Chapter 14

The evening came to its natural conclusion by 11pm. Conscious of the long day ahead, most owners and trainers alike wanted an early night in preparation for the big day. However not Miranda Cavendish! For her, the evening had got off to a bad start when she saw Clare emerge from her hotel. In her mind, Clare normally a scruffy stable lass, had gone out of her way to outshine Miranda. Then to add insult to injury, not only had James and Alistair complimented her but then every man at the Survetta had stolen a second look at her. Jealous and disgruntled, she had over indulged and after her sixth glass of wine and a liqueur coffee, Miranda was looking a little worse for wear. Despite this, she was insisting on going to the bar to meet Dean, Darren and Michelle.

"We simply must. I'm not ready for my bed yet. Come on, it's a holiday. What's the matter with all of you?" She stood on the stone steps waiting for a taxi in the cold February air.

"I don't mind going for one," said James in an effort to shut her up in front of the remaining guests.

"Sssuper!" slurred Miranda, hanging onto Alistair for balance.

Rolling her eyes at James, Clare knew she was in it for the long haul. One more drink wouldn't make any odds and she felt bad that Michelle hadn't been able to attend the dinner. It would be only right to meet with her and the lads before sloping off back to her bed.

The taxi drew up and the porter opened the door for them. Miranda took a step forward and as she did, missed the first step altogether. Her stiletto caught the tip of the step and losing her balance, she tripped

down the remaining five. Her handbag flew through the air, scattering its contents across the stone steps. She landed on top of James as he bent into the cab sending him tumbling forwards, shins cracking down onto the bottom sill of the door.

"Jesus Christ Miranda! What are you doing woman?" he barked. "Alistair, sort your wife out will you?" Rubbing his shins and dusting off his trousers, he turned to quickly gather her belongings. The porter and Alistair scrabbled around on the steps retrieving lipsticks and hair clips as quickly as possible so as not to draw attention to the embarrassing situation.

Miranda looked sheepish as Alistair bundled her into the back of the taxi. Shifting along the seats to give her more space, Clare couldn't help but laugh. Here they were, all dolled up like royalty and the ugly sister, so desperate to make a good impression had failed miserably. She had succeeded only in making herself a laughing stock.

"Don't you dare laugh at me. It's your bloody fault anyway!" Miranda wailed spitting her words at Clare. "Sitting there like, like,… ….Princess Diana! You love this don't you?"

"No Miranda. To be honest, I don't. I'd much rather be tucked up in bed in my pyjamas with my copy of 'Horse and Hound.' It's not my fault you drank too much and fell over; I was in the taxi already and nowhere near you! Perhaps you should try a lower heel and a smaller wine glass!" In an out of character blast, Clare told Miranda exactly how it was.

The silence in the taxi was crushing. Miranda sat in shame, whilst Alistair and James squirmed and stared fixedly out of their windows, studiously avoiding eye contact. Pulling up outside the Hotel Soldanella where Dean and Darren were staying, they all clambered out. Having sobered up slightly, Miranda straightened her dress and minced defiantly into the bar. Not wanting Miranda to spoil James' night, Clare got in the first round, while James went off in search of Dean, Darren and Michelle.

Darren Marcus was Dean's side kick. Having grown up together, Darren had watched as Dean's career blossomed. Although not a rider himself, he appreciated the skill and effort required to make it as a jockey and was prepared to support his friend through thick and thin. A small builder by trade, he was able to take time off from his current project to travel with Dean to St. Moritz. He enjoyed the party side of the racing world and had accompanied Dean to many a good knees up. Darren was the steady reliable force behind Dean and knowing him as well as he did, knew that Dean was feeling the pressure of the big race looming. It was a massive stepping stone for his friend and back at the hotel room Dean had confided in Darren that he was worried about his lack of experience on snow.

Darren had reassured him, telling him that he should view it as, 'just another race.' Bolstering him with a methodical, well thought out point of view he told Dean that:

a) He knew the horse.

b) The horse had run on the snow.

c) Horse and jockey were both fit to run
and…

d) No matter what else happened, it was one day in his life that he should try to enjoy.

"After all," he had said to Dean, "It's not very often we get an all-expenses paid trip to St. Moritz is it? Relax mate, you'll be fine. If that horse is as good as you seem to think he is, then you'll ace it!"

They had met with Michelle earlier that evening and propped up the hotel bar whilst waiting for the others to join them. In an effort to mask his nerves, Dean had started a drinking game. Downing the local speciality, a delicious concoction of Swiss chocolate almond liqueur, Crème de Cacao and Kahlua, needless to say they were all legless by the time the rest of the party joined them. James finally found Darren playing a huge black grand piano, with Dean and Michelle draped across the top singing the Whitney Houston ballad, "I will always love you!"

Finding it extremely funny, James' mood lightened. It was refreshing to be back in the company of these three clowns who were clearly enjoying their evening. Clare caught up with him, carrying a drinks tray.

"Quick, take these," she said thrusting the tray at James. She then jumped onto the stage and joined in with the awful howling coming from Dean and Michelle! It was late and the bar was virtually empty save for a couple of locals. They could sing like crying cats all night if they wanted to and not disturb a soul.

Miranda and Alistair plonked themselves next to James in a corner

booth with synthetic diner style seats. The conversation was a little stilted to begin with after the tripping episode but Alistair soon started to quiz James on tactics for the race.

"How do you plan to run him tomorrow James?"

"Same as normal, Dean needs a clear break. Buzz likes his head in front and he needs to get the job done." James was matter of fact in his response.

"What about him running properly on the snow?" Alistair asked.

"To be honest Alistair, he either will or he won't. My instinct tells me though that he will. Look we've gone through this a thousand times. He's right for the job."

"So you say, but is Dean?" Looking over at him belting out a Tina Turner classic, Alistair was right. He wasn't exactly conveying an air of professionalism.

"Dean has ridden him better than any of the other jockeys we've put up so far. He appreciates the horse and his ability and most importantly, he listens to instructions. He is our jockey of choice." Defending his decision, James made his point.

Miranda then piped up from across the table, "What if he doesn't get it right? What if he misses the break?"

"Then he'll have to ride his arse off, just like he would if he missed the break at Dunstall Park, or any other track for that matter!" Getting irritated James' tone was abrupt. His shins were still smarting following his last encounter with her, for which she had yet to apologise.

The conversation moved on and Miranda slipped away from the table. She headed over to the piano in what seemed like an attempt to join in the fun. Sidling up to Dean she whispered something quietly into his ear. He appeared not to have heard her the first time, over the noise of the piano assisted karaoke and leant back in to her as if asking her to repeat what she'd just said. Suddenly, loud shouting erupted into the room. The twang of the piano ground to a halt and all eyes turned to Dean as he flew into a rage.

"Listen here you spoilt bitch. You don't tell me how to ride tomorrow! I'm sick of you! In fact, you can ride your own bloody horse round that pond for all I care!"

Whatever Miranda had said to him, Dean had hit the roof. A boiling pot of nerves already, the pressure and alcohol, then the addition of

Miranda Cavendish and her vile behaviour had sent Dean spiralling off in an emotional rant. Trying to calm the little jockey down, Darren jumped off his stool and gripped him by the shoulders.

"Enough mate. Ignore her, she's drunk. Look its late now and it's a big day tomorrow. Let's call it a night."

Darren dragged Dean away in a torrent of abuse and bad language. The words, "Barbie doll," and "Plastic fantastic," could be heard clearly as Dean was forcibly removed from the bar, kicking and screaming.

"What on earth did you say to him Miranda?" boomed Alistair across the room.

"I told him that he'd better not lose tomorrow, that's all! I was only joking!" she replied, clearly unaware of the potential nightmare she had just caused.

If Dean refused the ride tomorrow on that basis, a replacement would need to be found and at such short notice it wouldn't be easy. Sure there were jockeys available but they didn't know Buzz and his way of going. A replacement jockey would not have time to either research him or build the bond that Dean had with him. Most importantly to Clare, they wouldn't respect him as Dean did.

James was livid. This woman had systematically ruined his evening. Embarrassing him in front of his peers at the Survetta, swooning over Lester Piggott like a love struck fool, falling down the steps and bruising her shins, insulting Clare and now, sending his jockey into a tail spin. She was a liability and he had had enough!

"Take your wife back to your hotel Alistair, sober her up and get her to bed before she upsets anyone else. I'll try and get Dean back on board, otherwise you'll be riding your own horse around the lake tomorrow. Christ woman, do you realise what you've done?"

Bursting into tears, Miranda fled the room in a typically attention seeking and dramatic fashion. Apologising, Alistair followed her like the dutiful husband he was. James pitied him. He had no backbone. Led around by the nose, by that unbearable woman would be a living hell as far as James was concerned. But James had no time for pity. In just over 12 hours, he had a horse entered for a race that could make his career as an independent trainer and right now he had no jockey.

Leaving Clare and Michelle in the bar, he made his way up in the lifts to Dean's and Darren's room, number 412 on the second floor.

The door was ajar and he found Dean slumped on the sofa, his head in his hands.

Darren was using the toilet with the door wide open and the room was a complete mess. Clothes were strewn everywhere, travel documents and yesterday's racing post littered the coffee table along with dirty cups and empty beer cans. The lads had been seriously enjoying their stay and James smiled as he remembered his time in Australia, his rooms looked exactly like this one. A bomb site!

Sitting down next to Dean he patted his knee.

"Come on lad, we're all half cut. Take no notice of that silly cow. She's talking out of her arse anyway."

"I tell you James, the way I'm feeling, I could walk out right now and I haven't even sat on him yet. What if I do miss the break like she said, then it's all over and we all go home empty handed." Dean was whinging now. He was drunk and feeling sorry for himself.

"Stop it you fool. You're not going to miss the break because Buzz won't! You know the craic mate. Let him do his job and he'll run for you tomorrow, just you wait and see. You and Clare go on about his power. Are you really going to walk away and watch some German lad take your place and win it? I don't think so!" James was pressing all of his buttons. "Now get your head down and I'll see you tomorrow morning. We can go for coffee, how about that?"

"Alright but keep that tart away from me! I don't give a shit if she's paying the bills, she's a nasty bitch!" Dean retorted bitterly as he hobbled over to his bed. Curling up like a child, he looked so small and vulnerable that James could understand his nerves. Dean had a good point. He hadn't even sat on Buzz for weeks, let alone gallop him on the snow.

Having smoothed troubled waters as best he could, James bade Darren good night and returned to Clare and Michelle at the bar. Looking up at him for news, James assured them that he had calmed Dean down. He was confident, that provided they could keep Miranda and Dean apart tomorrow, the lad would ride. Clare was relieved as exhausted by the huge highs and lows of the last few days, part of her longed for it to be over. She longed for them to be back in the lorry and going home, back to the normality and sanctuary of Dunstall Park and her little Rascie. These people were all far too high maintenance for Clare to be bothered with and she admired James' patience and resolve. Despite his own personal emotions about the race, James had managed to defuse the situation that evening with lightening efficiency. To Clare it demonstrated just how much he wanted to succeed on the ice.

Retiring back to their separate hotels, both Clare and James, felt a strange blend of exhaustion and anticipation. Both were physically drained by the long days but mentally spinning and reeling from the drama of the last 24 hours. Tomorrow would reveal all and they needed to sleep. Drifting off, James pictured Buzz being overtaken by Zatoof on the home straight…..Clare however pictured the glint in Buzz's eye and felt the fire in his belly.

Chapter 15

Sunday 23rd February 2003

6.30am

Opening her eyes, Clare lay perfectly still. Her first thoughts of the morning flooding her mind: a reminder to her of where she was and what she was doing here. Today was race day! Today Buzz would run under James' name, wearing Cavendish colours with Dean Wellings as his pilot. Today Buzz would run!

James was already up and awake. Smoking his third cigarette and on his second cup of coffee of the morning, he didn't know what to do with himself. He knew Clare would take care of Buzz and that his job would be to keep Alistair and Miranda away from Dean. Skiing sprang to mind. They had a long time to wait until the race preparations would begin around 1.30pm. They should get away and escape to the slopes for the morning. Dean certainly needed the mental break, as did Clare; he knew she'd be like a cat on hot bricks. Although slow to admit it, he too needed some space, more than anyone. The pressure as a trainer was often crippling but the last few days had topped his career to date. The owners were a nightmare and Buzz's quarter crack had thrown a shadow over the entire trip. The jockey was a bundle of nerves and Clare looked like she needed a six month sabbatical. In the middle of all of this, trying to hold it all together was one man alone, James Unett, and that man needed some skiing.

Darren placed a steaming cup of coffee on the bedside table next to Dean as he slept. The smell of the freshly ground beans gradually reached his nose, stirring him from the 'Land of Nod.' Sitting up in bed and thanking Darren, Dean sipped at his coffee. His head was thumping and his throat raw after the drinking and singing from the night before. That bitch had upset him. She'd really got into his head but today was not the day to be preoccupied with the petty goings on. Today was race day and he was going to be on board Buzz as they made their bid for the Grosser Preis. As the realisation hit him, he felt sick and rushing to the toilet he made it just in time before the previous evening's chocolate shots came back up to say hello!

Alistair ate breakfast alone. He intended to take Miranda shopping when she woke up. The group had all been living in each other's pockets and some space and time might put some much needed distance between them and last night's arguments. Not wanting the jockey to bail out, he made the executive decision to keep Miranda out of the way and for that he would need his cheque book and a map of the town centre. It was simple. After all, if Buzz won the prize pot he would be well able to afford it!

****

It didn't take James long to find Clare. Watching her as she went about her duties, he thought how attentive she was to Buzz, how affectionate and absorbed Clare was in the world that was Buzz.

"Good morning Jonesy! How's he doing today?" he said trying to sound relaxed.

"Hello! I didn't think I'd see you this early. Trouble sleeping?" she asked knowingly.

"Nope! Slept like a log," he lied. "I'm up because you all need a break from here. I thought a spot of skiing might be the answer and for those who'd rather just watch there's a café at the foot of the second slope. Let's get Dean up there for a couple of hours, away from Miranda."

"What was she playing at last night? That woman's got a serious problem, she is so conceited!" said Clare shaking her head, remembering in disbelief how badly Miranda had behaved. Once she had fed him, all she had to do was wait for the farrier to come and refit his shoe, then the vet would rewrap it which wouldn't take long, and

then she would be free until early afternoon. No point sitting on a bale staring at him for four hours until race time. She may as well go and watch James and have a coffee with Michelle and the lads.

The farrier and vet's visit took a little over an hour; the crack was holding up well and re-shoeing him was straightforward. Buzz was fresher than ever after another good night's rest but he stood and allowed them to treat his foot without complaint. It was almost as though he knew how important it was to get it right today.

****

The cable car hung in the air, swinging like a pendulum with the four inside. High above the slopes it jolted to a start and up they went. The view across the valley was spectacular and forcing herself not to look down, Clare once again admired the natural beauty surrounding her. They had an almost bird's eye view of the track and Clare could see that the race stalls had now been dragged into position. The little man on his snow smoothing machine was trundling around the track preparing the surface and there was once again life in the tented village. Forcing it out of her mind, Clare looked onward up the mountain. St. Moritz lays claim to over 350 kilometres of slopes and Clare had read that there were more than 30 mountain restaurants situated right next to the pistes. Headed for the Alpina Hutte, James had advised them to try the Alpine Macaroni, a local dish that complemented the cheesy fondue brilliantly.

Sporting a ski suit and mask, James was ready for action; he had rented his skis that morning and was grumbling about his sore shins after Miranda's stunt on the Survetta steps. He had them laughing as he recounted the fall like a slow motion clip, imitating her flying through the air in a haphazard fashion.

At the stop, James pointed the gang over to the Hutte and he slipped onto the ski lift to carry on up the piste. Relieved that the morning had gone to plan so far he sucked in a deep breath of the fresh mountain air. He could almost taste the purity as it hit his lungs. The sky was a brilliant blue, the odd cotton wool cloud hanging in the sky. Perfect, he thought. All I need now is a winner! Hardly daring to believe it could happen, he pushed off the lift and side stepped across to the top of the piste. Looking down across the valley he felt the weight of his worries lift from his shoulders. Pushing off he started his decent, leaning and bending with each turn, he zipped along seamlessly.

From the Hutte Clare had been watching him, following his line as he seamlessly whizzed down the mountainside. She had never seen him ski, although she knew he could she hadn't appreciated just how adept he was. She watched the path he carved through the snow, wondering if today they would really carve a path, a path in racing history.

The Alpina Macaroni was delicious. Tucking into the cheesy fondue which had become a firm favourite with them all, and the regional breads and flavoured cheeses the group were distracted from the day's schedule. Dean was feeling brighter, resigned to the fact he would not get to ride Buzz before the race. As always, the points Darren had made the day before made perfect sense. He needed to get on and ride Buzz like he always did; relaxed and free, let him get ahead and let him fly.

Michelle had been somewhat lost in all the drama. She had been thoroughly enjoying her night when Miranda had rocked up and spoilt it. Already disliking the woman after hearing Clare's and James' accounts of her and seeing the woman in action once or twice at Dunstall Park, Michelle found it a struggle to be civil to her. Michelle could see how wrecked Clare was from the travelling and the stress of Buzz's quarter crack, to see her more upset over Miranda's and Dean's squabble made Michelle dislike her even more. Quietly pleased it would all be over the following day, Michelle hoped Buzz would run a reasonable race and come out of it fit and well. Not one for confrontation and bad feeling, she was looking forward to going home where all the drama would fizzle out.

The conversation was light. Chatting over horses from their pasts and a new trainer to their area at home, the four companionably idled the time away. James buzzed up and down the mountain for another hour while they looked on. An onlooker would have seen a happy picture, the four relaxing in the winter sun, whilst the fifth group member enjoyed some skiing. However, if you looked more closely, you would have noticed them individually checking their watches. Repeatedly watching the time tick by, each and every one of them putting on a brave face but underneath it all the tick tock of the clock brought them closer and closer to the race.

Miranda and Alistair wandered through the town. She had a terrible headache and it was made worse by the disappointed look on her mature husband's face. He didn't moan or grumble but remained quiet and reserved and she knew he disapproved of her behaviour. Like a naughty girl who had been caught doing something she shouldn't, she tiptoed around him complimenting his choice of shoes and matching tie. It wasn't washing with Alistair; he just wanted to keep the peace. He had a lot of money at stake here and after turning down the sale of Buzz earlier in the year, he really hoped the gamble would pay off.

They walked along the Via Serlas, home to all the leading fashion designers from Chanel and Gucci to Louis Vuitton. All of the prestigious names on the international fashion scene were lined up together along the intimate street. Alistair traipsed through boutique after boutique throughout the morning until he could carry no more. Revelling in the glamour, Miranda had forgotten her attempt at remorseful behaviour and reverted back to selfish spendthrift. Purchasing belts, hand bags and knee length leather boots she spent her husband's cash without compunction.

1.15pm

Running her fingers down the front of his face Clare held Buzz close. The smell of him and the feel of his silky coat usually relaxed her like a drug. Not today. Today she wouldn't relax until it was done.

She wanted to tell him, in words he understood, just how important today was: wishing she could explain how he could trust in Dean, how he could gallop on the snow and show the world what a talented horse he was.

Buzz would need to take a leap of faith today. In less than two hours now, it would all be over. The race would be finished and there would be a winner. She wanted that winner to be Buzz so badly, she could feel it, almost tangible in the air.

Using her goat's hair brush, she brushed his head and face. He loved this part of the grooming process, enjoying the soft bristles as they massaged his forehead and around his eyes. She rubbed him down; he stood immaculate and gleaming in his stable. Placing his bridle over his head, pulling his forelock through and grooming it down, she kissed him on the soft part of his nose. His warm breath fanned against her cheek as she fastened the noseband and throat lash.

His one taped hoof remained untouched but the other three were gleaming with oil. She brushed his tail through until it felt like silk.

Wrapping his legs in black vet wrap, to protect them from injury, she wound it round and round each precious leg. She fitted his paddock sheet last. It was a yellow fleece with a green stripe. "JWU" was embroidered on the quarters to identify James as the trainer.

It was time to go.

2pm

Dean met James outside the weighing in room, and he handed in the colour bag with the silks and Buzz's blinkers and head gear. Dean would have to weigh in with all of these items. Buzz was to carry 9st 3lbs according to the officials, so that meant he would carry minimal lead. Dean weighed 8st 11lbs on a good day and James was praying he would be as near to the mark as possible once his saddle and the head gear were taken into account.

They didn't say much to each other, there were no words of comfort or assurance that would break either man from his feeling of isolation. Despite being surrounded by a heaving crowd, they both had their own demons to fight. Solitary focus on the job in hand was all they were both clinging to as the clock ticked steadily towards 2.45pm. Dean headed for the changing rooms and James to the pre parade ring where he would meet Clare to saddle up Buzz for the race.

2.15pm

Alistair and Miranda were parked at the bar inside the owners' tent, twitchy with anticipation Alistair repeatedly glanced over his shoulder at the walkway to catch the first glimpse of Buzz's arrival.

Miranda, perched on a high bar stool was also twitchy and on edge, not sure of the reception she would receive on meeting up with James for the first time after last night's argument. Sipping champagne prematurely, she reminded Alistair of a cat, sneaky and conniving. He was beginning to question why he had ever married her at all.

Michelle and Darren had opted to position themselves in the grandstand. Two tiers from the front and level with the finishing line, they had a perfect view of the track. Michelle had her camera at the ready, wanting to capture an action shot for Clare as a memento from the trip. She had placed their bets, including the Frenchmen's forty Euros. Buzz's odds were at 17/1. To show their support Michelle put €100 on him to win and Darren €75, although neither truly dared to believe he could win. In the distance, to the far right, Michelle could just pick out a chestnut horse with a yellow rug walking along the trackside. Buzz was on his way.

2.20pm

Leading him through the walkway between the stands, Clare strode out. Keeping up with him was not easy: his stride was long and far reaching and her small legs flashed back and forth trying to match his stride.

The pre parade ring was a large area set at the rear of the tented village. James was waiting by the entrance as Clare brought Buzz through. In front of them, a French horse called Etbash was being saddled by his trainer Weiss and to the right Christian was having trouble with Double Fun. The horse was clearly over excited by the crowd and was sweating profusely. Trying to get the saddle on him and keep him calm, Christian looked stressed and Clare sympathised with him. He had been kind to them during their visit but right now she couldn't help him.

Picking up on the excitement of the crowd, Buzz started to dance. As they circled the ring he kicked out, narrowly missing the rail. Clare hoped they wouldn't be in here much longer as he tensed and performed a huge fly buck. The bay horse following them, Borsato, was held back by his groom giving, 'The English horse' plenty of room to entertain the crowd. Round and round they went for what seemed like an eternity. A yellow rail enclosed the ring and Clare started to feel like a hamster on a wheel.

Spotting James entering the ring with his saddle, Clare slowed Buzz's pace to give James a chance to saddle him. She fitted his head gear and blinkers while James set about getting his saddle on. Kick, kick, kick went Buzz, his excitement starting to bubble over. Clare knew that all Buzz wanted was to be set loose on the track. He felt good, strong and keen but more than anything he felt ready.

2.30pm

From the pre parade ring, the horses were then led into the main paddock where Dean was waiting. Standing near to, but not next to, Alistair and Miranda, Clare could see he was nervous. James beckoned him across and Alistair and Miranda headed out to their private box to view to the race.

"Time to go lad, you ready?" he asked Dean.

"Yep! I'm ready. Is he Clare?" Dean asked almost frightened of the response.

"Sure he's ready Dean. You know how to ride him. Let him go, let him get his head in front and he'll do the rest." Clare sounded positive, sure of her answer and Dean took heart from it. One deep breath and a leg up later and Dean found himself on board. Slipping his feet into his irons, he could feel Buzz's energy. Clare was right, he was ready.

Then the bell rang, their cue to leave. This was it, the last moment Clare would have with him before he ran. The ache in her arm from holding him vanished and the nervousness she felt disappeared like the ripples on a pond. One hand on his neck and the other gripping the rein, Clare proudly led her Buzz out onto the track. Presenting him to the Grandstand, she turned him left out onto the track and slipping the lead rein off, she released him. Without hesitation, he bounced into a canter. Springing across the snow he looked superb. The commentator introduced him to the crowd as he passed by.

"Die Englische Pferd, Buzz, Nummer 3, von James Unett, Trainiert und geritten von Dean Wellings." Clare knew he was announcing Buzz's name and number and the trainer's and jockey's names. It was standard form for race meets but it was strange hearing it spoken in German! She had done all she could for him and Clare knew it was now Buzz's turn to shine. She had arranged to meet James on the scaffolding opposite the Grandstands and next to the finishing post. It was where most of the trainers stood to watch the race as it was the best vantage point for the whole track. She made her way over barely able to take her eyes from him as he cantered down to the stalls to be loaded.

Chapter 16

Buzz oozed presence and power as he burst onto the track. His conker coloured coat glowed like a torch against the snow. Dean's silks a vibrant green, yellow and red against the pure white back ground were shimmering and rippling around his tiny frame as the two figures fused into one along the track. Buzz looked magnificent, his figure cut through the crisp air, his warm breath billowed like a dragon breathing fire: he felt alive and ready. Ready for his run! The familiar feelings of strength and determination washed over Dean, stopping all his fears dead in their tracks. Heading for the stalls, he felt no hesitation in Buzz's stride; the quarter crack an irrelevance, not worth noting.

As the horses gathered around the rear of the stalls, Dean could not help but notice Number 1, Zatoof. The crowd had cheered him all the way down the track after his spectacular win here last year. He obviously had a strong fan base. The black horse overshadowed the field, his sheer size making him seem better than the rest. Drawn third, Zatoof would sit nearer to the inside rail. Buzz, had been drawn wide at eighth and was further to the left side of the stalls making it a longer run for him. It was crucial that Buzz made the break to avoid the snow being kicked up in his face from the horses in front or the race could be over before it had properly begun.

The stall handlers started loading the runners into the stalls and one by one they popped in. Then came Buzz's turn, he slipped quietly in. Calmness had taken over both horse and rider. Dean tuned into Buzz's steady breathing as he blocked all other sounds from his head. Buzz shuffled in the stall. Oblivious to the horses packed in on either side of him, the gleaming chestnut, focussed forwards by his blinkers, looked across the glaring white snow to the mountains beyond.

Ding! The bell sounded and the white metal stall doors sprang open, releasing the eager horses from within. Launching forwards with a huge leap, Buzz made no secret of his intentions. He broke cleanly away from the stalls and only Zatoof ran ahead as they took those first crucial strides along the track. Getting into his stride Buzz had almost forgotten he was galloping on snow and ice. For the horses tucked in behind them, there was a continuous cloud of snow and flying ice, a constant reminder of where they were.

Clare and James stood on the scaffolding. James couldn't bear to watch and stood with his back turned away from the runners, rolling a cigarette. Clare, his commentator, relayed the progress back to him.

"They're away and he's jumped clear! He's second James only Zatoof is ahead." Her excitement rang in the air. Clenching her hands into fists, she shook them in the air.

Dean knew there was more. He was travelling but he knew there was another gear to be had. Buzz was holding back. Maybe the uncertainty of the surface was hindering him but Dean didn't have time to dwell on it as they thundered down the straight. Approaching the grandstand Zatoof was nosing ahead. Dean was acutely aware of horses jostling behind him as the jockeys fought for prime positioning as they approached the first bend.

"He's tracking Zatoof. He's holding on. They're coming into the first bend now and he's still there," Clare prattled on like a child on a sugar rush.

Dean knew there was still a way to go and unless Buzz shifted up a gear now, they wouldn't make it. Around the first bend they went, Zatoof still a length in front. Down the back straight they thundered at an amazing pace, Buzz still running wide; his high action chopping through the soft snow like a knife through butter. The second bend loomed. Dean heeding James' warning, prepared for it to be tight and holding his position firm, he supported Buzz through it. Buzz could feel the harder more slippery ground beneath him and for self-preservation, backed off. As they came back onto the straight he had been over taken by Abash and Pessoa, sitting him in fourth position.

"They're round the second bend and it looks like he's backed off. Oh, no! He's dropped back, into fourth maybe fifth. I can't see for the bloody snow!" Clare moaned.

"Great! Bloody marvellous! Tracks the leader all the way then gets pipped to the post. It's a long drive home for a loser." James sighed with dismay and lighting his roll up shook his head.

Despite the flying snow, Dean knew they were nearly there, the Grandstand stood tall on the left. The crowd was screaming, but he couldn't hear them, they were muffled by the sound of Buzz's hoof beats as they battered the track. Determined to keep pushing Dean hollered at his mount.

"Come on lad, now, now, now! Go, Buzz, go!"

Sensing the urgency, Buzz pushed hard. From the bottom of his heart he ran. He dug deep, and found that extra gear. Quickening his pace, and lengthening his stride Buzz strode forward. The sound of his breathing and hoof beats blended into an urgent rhythm as he smashed down the straight. Breaking free from the field of leaders, moving into second place, there was only Zatoof left to beat. He powered on relentlessly, pushing and pushing, each stride gaining on the big black horse.

"James he's coming! He's coming through! Buzz! GO ONNNNN RUNNNNNN!" She screamed at him from the scaffolding, gripping the ironwork for dear life as she willed her beautiful boy on to the line.

Dean knew he could do it. Judging their speed and the distance remaining he realised they could nail it. Crouching low across his back, he let the horse fly. Stretching his hands forward, giving Buzz his head, he closed his eyes and willed him onward. They breezed up alongside Zatoof, head to head for a split second, but Buzz was travelling faster and they flew passed him and stormed over the line.

"He's WON, JAMES HE'S WON!!!!!" Clare grabbed him and scrabbled for the stairs, leaping from the scaffolding, they fell into the snow together, shocked but elated. He had done it! The stale moody horse of a few months ago had just become the first ever British trained horse to win a listed race at St. Moritz. More than that, he had done it because he wanted to and because Buzz was a true racehorse right down to the bone.

Dean couldn't stop him. Not content just with winning the race, Buzz wanted to show the crowds just exactly how fast he could go! Deciding he'd earned his right to run, Dean gave him his head, besides, he didn't have the strength to argue. Breathless and feeling a little faint, that was the most exhilarating ride of Dean's life. The acceleration

Buzz had found was phenomenal; the kind of reserve that all jockeys dream their rides will have. He was a serious horse and Dean was proud to have ridden him. Reeling from the experience though, he was glad to clap eyes on Clare who was hurtling along the straight in their direction.

She ran to them, full throttle and reaching up, threw her arms around Buzz's neck.

"You are amazing, my boy. What a win! What a bloody fantastic win! I knew you could do it, I never doubted you for a minute! You're a clever, clever, boy! That speed! Where did that come from eh? You kept that a secret, didn't you?"

For Dean, the world started to go fuzzy. Clare turned to congratulate him just in time as he was about to pass out. Slumped forward onto Buzz's neck, she balanced him on the saddle as she walked them proudly back over towards the deafening crowd.

James had to find the owners, which didn't take long. His head was swimming. Feelings of relief and immense pride washed over him. Walking through the crowds, people patted him on the back and congratulated him like an old friend. Reporters stuck microphones in his face and note pads under his nose, desperate for a quote from the winning horse's trainer. Deliberately ignoring them, James reminded himself of something his father had once told him:

"When a once in a lifetime event happens, take your time and enjoy it. Slow it down and savour it because they don't happen very often."

James intended to slow it down, down to a complete stand still. He was on cloud nine as he approached the enclosure. Miranda had already cornered Lester Piggott. He looked like he couldn't wait for the horse to arrive in order to get away from the mad woman who was virtually chewing on his ear. Alistair was cracking open a bottle of champagne, thrilled with his £23,000 win, he didn't care who Miranda offended. Anyway, he had decided to divorce her.

Michelle and Darren were weaving their way through the crowds, desperate to get down to the ringside to congratulate their friends. They were ecstatic with the win, Michelle had bagged €1,700, Darren had won €1,275, and the French Official had won €680! Michelle could see Clare leading Buzz through the walkway, back to the winners' enclosure to claim his rightful place in history. Dean slipped off Buzz's back. Still feeling light headed and woozy although a little more

human, he needed to weigh in and gather his wits together before the presentation was to take place. Giving Buzz an affectionate pat, he thanked him for the ride of his life and vanished into the weighing in room.

Overwhelmed, Clare was openly crying. Tears of pride ran down her freckled cheeks as she took her horse, her Buzz, into the enclosure. Cameras flashed in their faces as they walked under the huge 'White Turf' sign that hung above their heads. Buzz would be pictured in sports editorials worldwide after that performance. The 17/1, 'English Horse' had stunned the crowd. Against the odds, with a quarter crack and hardly any experience on the track, Buzz had proved to the world, on an international stage, exactly what could be achieved with just that extra little bit of effort!

In awe of the champion horse he had become, Clare couldn't take her eyes off her Buzz. The presentations were a blur. Her only concern at the moment was to prevent Buzz from kicking the brand new shiny black BMW that the sponsors had put in the ring. The presentation was hosted by Lester Piggott. Firmly gripping James' hand, he presented him with a carved glass trophy and a set of commemorative champagne flutes. Posing for photos with Alistair, James looked on smiling when Lester gave a weary looking Dean a huge bunch of flowers for his part in the race. He then assured Alistair and Miranda that the prize money would be transferred directly into their Weatherby's account.

Buzz stood, soaking it all up. The crowd and attention made him feel alive, as he had never felt before! Draped in a cooler sheet, emblazoned with 'American Express, Grosser Preis, Winner 2003,' he looked regal as the press flashed away.

Clare wanted to get Buzz back across to the barn. He had run a fabulous race and was in top form but he needed to recover and rest. His welfare was always paramount in her mind. Getting the nod from James, she prepared to make her way back out to the track for the last time. Leading him away from the crowds and back to the warm barn, Clare studied him in awe. She didn't think she'd ever have the chance to train a better horse. He was one in a million! They strolled across the snow, back to the barn; just her and him, quietly together, Clare Jones and her Buzz.

The End

GALLERY

Clare riding Fircone, her first pony

Home sweet home, Dunstall Park, far right

Ariel view of Dunstall Park

Bressbee's stable Dunstall Park

Bressbee

*Clare and **her** Buzz, Dunstall Park*

Haydock 9th August – Fight the Feeling winning

Wolvs Buzz winning 16th November

Tigress

26th December 2002 Bressbee wins

Boxing Day Wolvs Buzz wins

Clare and Buzz schooling over hurdles

Pride in Clares' eyes

Urban Myth

Bressbees' win January 31st Wolvs

Clare working Buzz on snow covered track Wolvs

Tiny

Rascal

James working Docksider in Hong Kong

James riding out

Rebecca Walters

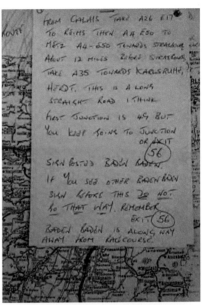

Bressbee's Transport Certificate

Handwritten notes to Baden Baden

Main image: Parade ring. (Inset) Snow Shoe note the three extra sections on the front and two on the ends of the shoes for extra grip in the snow

Skiing morning of race

Pre parade ring St. Moritz

Galloping during the race

Galloping through bend

Bressbee motoring home

Pulling up after his win

Clare and her champion

Walking back to winners enclosure

Clare, James, Jockey and Bressbee

Lester Piggot & Bressbee in winners' enclosure

Wearing winners' rug

Rebecca Walters

GLOSSARY

Aids – signal from rider to horse

Bay – brown horse with black legs/ mane/tail

Best Turned Out – best groomed horse

Bidding Claims – the process for purchasing a horse in a seller/claimer

Bit – a metal mouth piece used to control and communicate with a horse

Blew Up – lack of fitness, ran out of steam

Blindfold – used on the head of a horse if being difficult to load

Blinkers – a device used to shield a horses vision to improve forward focus

Bloodstock Agent – a thoroughbred horse dealer

Bolting – to gallop in fear of something, to run away

Bookies – Bookmakers

Box – alternative name for a stable

Breaking – the process of first riding a young horse

Bridged Reins – putting one rein over the top of the other, to form a small hoop about 10cms (4in) long, which you hold between your hands and which fits over the horse's neck.

Bridle – the device used on a horses' head whilst riding

Broke Stride – faltered within a pace

Broncing – a rodeo type action

Bucked – stand on front feet and kick rear feet in the air

Came Out Of – how the horse was after running a race

Canter – a three time gait

Chased Down – to catch up with

Chestnut – colouring akin to a red head

Chifney – an anti rear bit

Claiming Race – the trainer can take the horse back to optimum weight, but if it wins it can be claimed by a purchaser

Colic – abdominal pain

Colours – the owners individual racing colours

Colour Bag – used by trainers to carry the silks into the weighing in room Dam – mother of

Dapple Grey – grey/white mottled colouring

Declarations – horses that are officially announced as running in a race

Drawn – Stall number at the beginning of a race

Dressage – equestrian sport involving a series of movements between horse and rider

Dressed Over – groom/rug/bandage a horse

Dual Purpose – a horse that can run in either flat or national hunt races

Dug in – worked hard

Electrolytes – dissolvable sugars and salts for hydration

Eventing – equestrian sport involving dressage, show jumping and cross country

Exercise – being ridden and trained

Farrier – a person trained in fitting horseshoes

Favourites – the horse predicted to be the winner

Feed Manger – a stabled horses dinner bowl

Filly – young female horse under the age of four years

Flank – area on the horses' side

Flat Horse – a horse that is trained to run in flat races

Flat Hacing – races run on a track not involving jumps Fly buck – a huge buck

Fore – front leg Forwards into the bridle – a willing horse that is galloping well and accepting instruction, listening and moving forwards

Fresh – a keen and excited horse

Frog – sensitive part on the underside of a horses hoof Furlong – a distance, 201 metres galloping – the fastest of the horses gaits

Gelding – a male horse that has been castrated

Gets its blood up – something that excites and gets the pulse racing

Groom – person charged with daily care of horses

Hanging – a horse that doesn't run in a straight line and pulls left/right, hanging on the jockeys hands as he/ she does so

Havanna – colour description of brown leather

Hay – dried grass used as feed

Haylage Net – a string net used to hold feed, it is tied to a ring on the stable wall

Head Collar – a device placed on horses' heads used for leading them

Headgear – a head mask used to reduce down crowd noise

HH – hands high is the height measurement for horses

High rolling knee action – the horses' personal method of movement. *Bressbee has particularly high knee action*

Hind – back leg

Hind Quarters – the rear end of a horse

Hocks – hind leg joint on a horse

Hoof – horses' foot

Hoof Wall – side of the hoof

Hug rails – to run immediately alongside the track rails

International Racing Bureau – Organise international horse racing (IRB)

Iron Grey – colouring

Irons – see stirrups

Jockey Licence – issued to all professional and amateur jockeys to permit them to ride in races

Jump Racing – see National Hunt explanation

Kick Back – debris that flies from the hooves during galloping

Kick on – to canter away in a more pressing manner

Lame – partially or wholly immobile

Lead Rein – rope used for leading the horse from the ground

Lead up – to lead the horse around the paddock before the race

Leaning – a horse that uses his mouth against the bit and puts his head weight onto the bit

Left Handed – a track that you race around to the left

Length – measurement used to describe a horse from nose to tail, usually around 8 feet

Leg Up – assist a rider to get onto the horse

Loading – placing a horse in the stalls or on a horsebox Lost pace – slowed down

Make all – to get ahead

Mane – horses neck hair

Missed the break – didn't get out of the stalls fast enough

Mucked out – removing wet and soiled bedding from stables

National Hunt Racing – races involving jumps

National Hunt Yard – training yard specialising in training horses for jump races

Nearside – left

Noseband – part of the bridle that goes around the horses' nose novice – relatively inexperienced horse person or horse

Numnah – a cloth that fits under the saddle used to soak up sweat and make the saddle more comfortable

Offside – right

Owners & Trainers Lounge – area at tracks specifically for the owners and trainers of the horses

Paddock Sheet – rug used in the paddock to keep the horse warm during the parade

Parade Ring – area at the tack where the horses are exhibited before running

Partition – divides in a horsebox/ trailer

Pilot – jockey

Pipe opener – to gallop hard and to the fullest extent, known for clearing the heart and lungs

Placing – end results of a race, 2nd, 3rd, 4th

Plaited – plaites in the mane

Point to Point – no rules Jump racing

Polo – a team equestrian sport involving sticks, balls and goals

Polytrack – type of all weather surface

Producing – training and developing a horse

Quarter Crack – a crack in the side of the hoof wall

Race Card – printed information for the days races

Race fit – fit and ready to run in a race

Race Meets – racing events run over a day, be it afternoon/evening racing

Plates – aluminium horse shoes light weight specifically for racing racing

Post – industry magazine

Racing Stripes – experience in riding in races

Racing Tights – stockings worn by jockeys during races

Ramp – the access ramp of a horsebox

Rated – a horses' grade on a particular surface

Reins – the rider holds them in their hands, they communicate with the horse through them

Remained prominent – the horse ran ahead of the pack

Resident Trainer – a trainer that stables his horses and trains at the track

Ridden out his claim – to be a professional jockey you have to ride 100 races as an amateur, then you have ridden out your claim and can apply for a professional licence

Road Work – exercising horses around the roads rather than on the track

Rode hard – the jockey really pushed the horse

Rowing along – over riding in desperation

Rubber Reins – reins with a rubber coating for extra grip

Rump – horses rear end

Run cleanly – a horse that comes out of the stalls without issue and gallops along in the race in a text book fashion

Running – entered for a race

Running flat – no real effort

Running wide – taking a longer route away from the rail

Saddle – implement used by riders to sit on the horse

Saddle the horse – is to put the saddle on in the parade ring before a race

Schooling – educating/training a horse

Scoop – a measuring implement for horse feed

Seller – a race in which the winner is for sale to the highest bidder

Shavings – wood shavings used as a bedding material in stables

Show Jumping – equestrian sport involving a course of jumps

Shying/Spooking – a horse's reaction when he/she moves away from something that worries them

Silks – clothing worn by jockeys when racing, individual colours and designs owned by the horses owner

Sire/sired – father of/fathered by

Sitting pretty – waiting to strike during a race

Skipping out – remove dirty bedding from a stable

Soft hands – a jockey who is gentle with his hands and therefore the reins which are attached the metal bit inside the horses' sensitive mouth

Sound – in good mechanical health

Stalls – the device used to hold the horses at the start of races

Star – marking on the horses forehead

Steady away – to canter in a steady but progressive manner

Stirrups – iron feet holders for jockeys

Straw – used as bedding

Strong legs – a jockey who can use his legs effectively to communicate with the horse

Strong seat – a jockey who can sit well, and use his weight to communicate with the horse

Stud Farm – a farm dedicated to breeding horses

Sugar Beet – feed type, sloppy tasty and sugary

Sweat Rug – a cooling rug used to control temperature and absorb sweat after exercise

Sweating up – sweating after a race or die to anxiety

Tack cleaning – to clean the saddle/ bridle

Tack Room – room at a stable yard where the equipment is stored

Tacked up – putting the saddle/bridle on the horse

The trip – distance

Throatlash – part of the bridle that goes around the horses' throat

Top Door – the top half of a stable door

Trackside – next to the track

Trainers Tag – worn by all trainers at the races to identify them

Travel Sheet – a cooling blanket used during transit

Travelling now – increasing in speed and maintaining it

Trot – a two time gait

Trotter – breed of horse

Upsides – to ride alongside another horse

Weigh in – jockey's are weighed before and after races

Weight bearing – able to place weight on limb

Weatherbys – Administers racing under contract to the British Horseracing Board

Whickering – a form of communication by horses similar to neighing

Whipper in – member of the team in fox hunting

White Turf – Organisation that run the events at St. Moritz, and also refers to the track itself

Width/Bone – a horse that has a big frame and is thickset

Winners' enclosure – an area at the track that the race winners go to be congratulated after running

Working canter – a good strong canter fairly fast

Working straight – a horse that works in a straight methodical manner around the track

Yard – stable yard

Yearling – a 1 year old horse